REPTILE AND AMPHIBIAN VARIANTS
COLORS, PATTERNS, AND SCALES

REPTILE AND AMPHIBIAN VARIANTS
COLORS, PATTERNS, AND SCALES

H. Bernard Bechtel, M.D.

KRIEGER PUBLISHING COMPANY
MALABAR, FLORIDA
1995

Original Edition 1995

Printed and Published by
KRIEGER PUBLISHING COMPANY
KRIEGER DRIVE
MALABAR, FLORIDA 32950

Copyright © 1995 by Krieger Publishing Company

FROM A DECLARATION OF PRINCIPLES JOINTLY ADOPTED BY A COMMITTEE OF THE AMERICAN BAR ASSOCIATION AND A COMMITTEE OF PUBLISHERS:

This publication is designed to provide accurate and authoritative information in regard to the subject matter covered. It is sold with the understanding that the publisher is not engaged in rendering legal, accounting, or other professional service. If legal advice or other expert assistance is required, the services of a competent professional person should be sought.

Library of Congress Cataloging-In-Publication Data

Bechtel, H. Bernard, 1922–
    Reptile and amphibian variants: colors, patterns, and scales/by
H. Bernard Bechtel
      p. cm.
    Includes bibliographical references (p.) and index.
    ISBN 0-89464-862-4 (acid free paper)
    1. Reptiles—Variation. 2. Amphibians—Variation. 3. Reptiles—
Color. 4. Amphibians—Color. 5. Captive reptiles—Breeding.
6. Captive amphibians—Breeding. 7. Color-variation (Biology)
8. Scales (Reptiles) I. Title.
QL645.5.B43 1995
597.9′04158—dc20   93-10677
                                  CIP

10 9 8 7 6 5 4 3 2

This book is dedicated to my wife, Bette,
and to our friends, Sherm and Madge Minton.

A narrow Fellow in the Grass
Occasionally rides—
You may have met him—did you not
His notice sudden is—

The Grass divides as with a Comb—
A spotted shaft is seen—
And then it closes at your feet
And opens further on—

He likes a Boggy Acre
A floor too cool for Corn—
Yet when a Boy, and Barefoot—
I more than once at Noon

Have passed, I thought, a Whip lash
Unbraiding in the Sun
When stooping to secure it
It wrinkled, and was gone—

Several of Nature's People
I know, and they know me—
I feel for them a transport
Of cordiality—

But never met this Fellow
Attended, or alone
Without a tighter breathing
And Zero at the Bone—

Emily Dickinson

Contents

Preface

This book is about observable anomalies of reptiles and amphibians, many if not most of which are caused by gene mutations. Mutations are ubiquitous among organisms and are the prerequisite for normal variation, adaptation, and evolution. However, some rare mutations result in the significant deviations from normal that are discussed and illustrated in this book.

Reptiles and amphibians with conspicuously altered colors and patterns are usually astonishing and often beautiful. They have fascinated me since I saw my first albino black snake at a roadside zoo in the 1930's. Albinism is one of the more striking variants, and probably the best known, but it is only one of many.

My wife, Bette, and I have always kept captive reptiles and amphibians, mostly snakes, in our home. We have been breeding snakes continuously since 1955, starting with corn snakes. Most of the breeding has been for the determination of the genetics of variants. Through these years, we have had a succession of bizarre and beautiful snakes in our home. We have bred many generations of several genera, and together and singly have published our findings.

Reptiles and amphibians are a big part of our life. In the course of our investigations, we have raised hundreds of baby snakes, taken care of numerous health problems among them, and become familiar with the problems peculiar to captive snakes. Our vacations have consisted almost entirely of herpetological meetings and informal field trips. I cannot pass by a sheet of corrugated metal without turning it over to see what may be under it.

As my interest in anomalous reptiles and amphibians became known through occasional talks to local herpetological societies and our various publications, colleagues began to tell me about additional aberrant specimens. As the information was channeled my way, I became somewhat of a repository for reports and photographs of odd specimens. If nothing else, I have learned that anomalous reptiles and amphibians are more common than most people are aware of, and the deviations from normal more diverse than I suspected when my interest began. Between color, pattern, scales, and combinations of these, there are enormous possibilities for error, and if something can go wrong, sooner or later it will.

I am constantly asked questions. "Why is it blue?" "Why aren't its eyes red?"

"What will happen if I breed this snake with a melanistic snake?" "What is tyrosinase?" "Where can I find one?" And most often, "Is there a book somewhere that I can read about this?" General herpetology texts and books do not focus on the abnormal, and I know of no book that enlarges on this subject. I hope that this book answers some of the questions.

The book is essentially an amplification of the talks that I have presented to various herpetological groups, and covers this arcane subject from my personal perspective. Material has been gleaned from general herpetological literature and texts, and the few sources of more specific information regarding pigmention and anomalies. I have drawn freely on my own experiences and observations, and also on those of friends and colleagues. The field is complex and incompletely understood. In the light of present knowledge, there is no adequate explanation for many of the variants discussed and illustrated in this book. There is not even a consensus on terminology. Any oversimplification in subject matter is to help general readers understand it. If nothing else, the book illustrates voids in my knowledge.

Variant reptiles and amphibians are inextricably associated with husbandry and captive breeding. When an anomalous specimen is located, it is human nature to want to know more about it, and if the anomaly is hereditary. When numbers are insufficient for statistical analysis, captive breeding is the only way to find out if the variant is genetic. Furthermore, people who see some of these animals want one for themselves, and they cannot reasonably expect to collect one. As a result, a captive breeding industry has arisen to satisfy this demand.

Chapters on general herpetology, structure and function of skin, and chromatophore biology are included to provide a basis for understanding the variants. Since many of the aberrancies are caused by mutations, a chapter on genetics has been added for the benefit of readers unfamiliar with the principles and terminology of genetics.

Books and references used in preparing the text are listed at the back of the book. Where specific anomalies are discussed, the relevant published observations and references are cited at the end of the chapter, and personal communications are acknowledged in the text. All reptiles and amphibians are referred to by their common name except for the first mention of a species, where the scientific name is included.

Regarding many of the illustrations in this book, I have not seen the actual specimens. I have labeled them on the basis of what I think they represent, what they look like, or what the photographer called them. In some, the anomaly is obvious. A coal black variant of a reptile or amphibian that normally has a color pattern is easy to label melanistic. Others are not so simple, and there is no accepted term for many of those that are unique or known by only two or three specimens. Readers are free to interpret the anomalies as they see them.

The word *we* in this book, unless otherwise specified, refers to Bette and me.

Acknowledgments

My wife, Bette, has accompanied me on nearly every field trip, and has helped tend the hundreds of snakes that we have raised, in spite of the fact that she was not the least interested in reptiles when we got married. She has been a full partner in every aspect of this book. Her name is not on the title page because she insists that this is my book.

I owe a particular debt to Bill Love of Alva, Florida. Bill sent me hundreds of his slides of reptiles and amphibians, permitting me to choose any that would be useful for this book. In addition, he published a request for slides in his business circular, providing me with many illustrations that I never would have found otherwise.

Ellen Belz of the Chicago Herpetological Society was also gracious enough to publish a request for slides in the Chicago Herp Bulletin. This provided me with additional illustrations.

The following persons made this book possible by permitting me to use their illustrations: Carl Anthony; Al Baldogo; Karl Barke; Steve Barten; Richard Bartlett; Jeffrey Howard Black; Alvin Braswell; Glen Carlzen; Bill Christie; Bob Clark; Larry Collier; Jeanette Covacevich; Dale Cronwell; Tom Crutchfield; Kevin Enge; Ron Everhart; David Fitzgerald; Dick Flood; Paul Freed; Richard Funk; James Gerholdt; Bill Girden; Greg Greer; Michael Hammock; Dan P. Johnson; Glen Johnson; Pete Kahl; Andrew Koukoulis; Michael Lodato; Greg Longhurst; Gary P. Lorio; William H. and Kathy Love; Peter Mayne; Craig McIntyre; Kenneth Mierzwa; Sherman A. Minton; Pat Murphy; Michael Oldham; Manny Rubio; Gerard Salmon; William Smith; James Tuten; Thomas F. Tyning; Terry Vandeventer; Jaime Villa; John Walling; Trooper Walsh; Thomas Weidner; Jeff Wines; Mark Worthy; Jeffrey Yohe; and Rich Zuchowski.

Illustrations used are acknowledged. I was not able to use all of them, mostly because of duplications. I sincerely apologize for this.

Sara Fornes and Teresa Lanier, my office assistants, in addition to their usual duties, typed letters and helped in many ways.

About the Author

Dr. Bechtel was born in New Enterprise, Pennsylvania. Aside from years spent in education and military service, he lived most of his life in Johnstown, Pennsylvania until moving to Georgia in 1963. He received his Bachelor of Science degree from the University of Pittsburgh, his medical degree from Jefferson Medical College of Philadelphia, and his specialty training at Indianapolis General Hospital. He is a Fellow in the American Academy of Dermatology and maintains a practice in Valdosta, Georgia.

Glossary

Aberrant: deviating from the ordinary, normal, or expected.

Adaptation, Biological: alteration of structure or function to suit a particular environment.

Albino: an organism with absent or deficient melanin.

Allele: either of the two paired genes affecting an inherited trait.

Alleles, Multiple: in a given population, more than two alternative forms of a gene affecting a single inherited trait.

Allopatric: related populations occupying mutually exclusive but usually adjacent geographical areas.

Amelanistic: containing no melanin.

Amino Acid: organic compounds that are the building blocks of protein.

Amphibian: capable of living both in water and on land, typified by frogs, toads, and salamanders.

Amplexus: clasping of female amphibians by males in copulatory embrace.

Anerythristic: without red color.

Anomaly: a deviation from the ordinary, normal, or expected.

Anuran: amphibians lacking tail in adult stage; frogs and toads.

Aposematic Coloration: warning coloration.

Aquatic: living or growing in water.

Arboreal: living in trees.

Arthropod: a member of a large phylum of invertebrates, characterized by exoskeleton and jointed legs, typified by insects and spiders.

Artificial Selection: selective breeding to perpetuate desirable traits.

Autosomal Mutation: a gene change occurring in any cell other than a sex cell.

Autotomy: self-amputation, typified by tail loss of some lizards when attacked.

Axanthism: absence of yellow color, or absent or deficient xanthophore pigment metabolism.

Backcrossing: mating of an organism with a parent.

Bicephaly: possessing two heads.

Bilateral: occurring on both sides of an organism.

Biological Clock: innate physiological or behavioral rhythms synchronized with recurrent environmental factors such as time or day.

Carapace: dorsal portion of shell of turtle.

Carnivorous: meat-eating.

Carotenoid: any group of red and yellow pigments, chemically similar to carotene, contained in animal fat and some plants.

Caruncle: horny spine on upper jaw of hatchling turtle, used to slit shell for hatching.

Caudal: pertaining to the tail or posterior end.

Chromosome: nuclear inclusion containing genes arranged in linear sequence.

Chromatophore: pigment cell.

Congenital: present at or before birth, not necessarily inherited.

Crossing Over: exchange of corresponding segments of homologous chromosomes during meiosis, so the resulting gametes will contain chromosomes with information from both parents rather than one or the other.

Cryptic: concealing or camouflaging.

Cutaneous: pertaining to the skin.

Dendrite: a protoplasmic projection extending from a cell body.

Deoxyribonucleic Acid (DNA): a molecule containing the genetic information of all living cells. The unit of inheritance. Gene.

Differentiation: progressive changes in cell, tissue, or organ structure and function during development, usually from simple to more complex.

Dihybrid Cross: mating of individuals heterozygous for two separate inherited traits.

Dimorphism: occurrence of two forms, distinct in color or other characteristic, among animals of the same species.

Diploid: refers to cells with pairs of homologous chromosomes (somatic cells).

Diurnal: active during daylight.

Dominant: an allele that can determine the phenotype whether heterozygous or homozygous.

Dopa: 3,4-dihydroxy-L-phenylalanine, an intermediate chemical in the synthesis of melanin.

Dorsal: the top, back, or uppermost surface of an organism.

Ectothermic (also **poikilothermic** or **cold-blooded**): possessing no internal means for controlling body temperature.

Embryo: organism in early stages of development, before it is physiologically independent.

Embryogenesis: the development and growth of an embryo.

Endothermic (also **homeothermic** or **warm-blooded**): having ability to maintain constant body temperature in different ambient temperatures.

Erythrophore: red chromatophore.

Eumelanin: black or brown melanin.

External Fertilization: union of sperm and egg outside the body of either parent.

F_1: first generation offspring.

F_2: second generation offspring.

Femoral: pertaining to thighs or femur.

Flash Color: bright and conspicuous patch of color on an otherwise drab animal, displayed briefly to distract predators.

Gamete (also **germ cell**): mature haploid egg or sperm.

Gene: unit of inheritance (DNA), carried on chromosomes.

Gene Pool: collectively, all of the alleles of all the genes in a population.

Genetics: study of heredity.

Genotype: genetic makeup of an organism.

Germ Cell (also **gamete**): mature haploid egg or sperm.

Gravid: pregnant.

Habitat: specific place within range in which an organism lives.

Haploid: having a single set of chromosomes (germ cell or gamete).

Hemoglobin: an iron-containing protein in red blood cells primarily for oxygen transport.

Hemotoxin: substance poisonous to or destructive of vascular system and contents.

Herbivorous: relying on vegetation for food.

Hereditary: capable of being transmitted from generation to generation.

Herpetoculture: breeding and husbandry of reptiles and amphibians.

Herpetology: study of reptiles and amphibians.

Heterozygous: having nonidentical alleles for the trait in question.

Homeothermic (also **endothermic** or **warm-blooded**): having ability to maintain body temperature at different ambient temperatures.

Homologous: corresponding in origin, structure, and position.

Homozygous: having identical alleles for the trait in question.

Hybrid: offspring of parents that differ in one or more heritable characters. Also refers to offspring of parents of different species.

Hypomelanistic: containing decreased amount of black and brown melanin.

Hypopigmented: containing decreased amount of pigment.

Indicator Species: a species that manifests by its presence in its habitat the existence of certain environmental conditions.

Intergrade: an intermediate form exhibiting a combination of the characteristics of two separate subspecies of the same species.

Intermedin: hormone secreted by the intermediate lobe of the pituitary gland, known to control in part the size and activity of some chromatophores.

Internal Fertilization: union of sperm and egg inside the female parent.

Iridophore: iridescent chromatophore that produces color by physical rather than metabolic methods.

Keratin: tough protein outermost layer of skin.

Keratinocyte: general term for epidermal cell.

Lateral Line Organ: series of sense organs along sides of some amphibians, probably for detection of currents, vibrations, and pressure.

Leucistic: white.

Linkage, Genetic: tendency of certain alleles to be inherited together due to the fact that they are located on the same chromosome.

Locus: position of a gene on a chromosome.

Meiosis: type of cell division in which a diploid cell divides twice, resulting in haploid germ cells.

Melanin: black or brown pigments synthesized from tyrosine.

Melanism: unusual darkening of normal pigmentation due to increased melanin.

Melanocyte: sole pigment cell of warm-blooded animals, the function of which is to synthesize melanin.

Melanocyte Stimulating Hormone (MSH): secretion of anterior pituitary gland that stimulates synthesis of melanin.

Melanophore: chromatophore of cold-blooded vertebrates that produces melanin.

Melanosynthesis: production of melanin within melanophores or melanocytes.

Metamorphosis: transformation of one distinctive stage in life history to another, as in tadpole to frog.

Microhabitat: small restricted part of the entire range that is utilized by an organism.

Mitosis: cell division with each daughter cell identical to the parental cell.

Monohybrid Cross: breeding experiment in which parents differ in only one genetically determined trait.

Morph: visible form and structure of an organism.

Morphologic: pertaining to form and structure of an organism.

Mutagen: any substance capable of altering genetic information.

Mutation: an abrupt change in the base sequence of DNA, resulting in new genetic information. If the mutation is in a gamete, the new genetic information can be passed to the next generation.

Natural Selection: differential reproduction and survival of organisms due to environmental forces, resulting in preservation of traits most fitted for survival.

Neoteny: retention of juvenile characteristics by sexually mature individuals.

Neural Crest: dorsal portion of the neural tube (the primitive nervous system) that produces undifferentiated pigment cells and the peripheral nervous system.

Neurotoxin: poisonous substance affecting the nervous system.

Niche: that particular part of the total environment utilized by an organism.

Nocturnal: active by night.

Nonallelic genes: not coded for the same trait; not paired.

Omnivorous: including both plants and animals in diet.

Ontogenetic: development of an individual organism. Changes occurring during postembryonic life are ontogenetic.

Oviparous: reproducing by laying eggs.

Paedomorphosis: retention of juvenile characteristics by sexually mature individuals.

Parthenogenesis: mode of asexual reproduction, in which embryo develops without fertilization.

Phaeomelanin: red or yellow melanin.

Phenotype: an organism described by its external appearance.

Physiology: science dealing with function of organisms and their parts.

Piebald: spotted or patched, usually in black and white.

Plastron: ventral shell of turtle.

Poikilothermic (also **ectothermic** or **cold-blooded**): having no internal means for controlling body temperature.

Polymorphic: occurrence together of two or more distinct morphological forms of a species.

Postpartum: following birth.

Prepartum: preceding birth.

Proteolytic: capable of breaking down protein.

Pteridine: class of chemicals incorporated in xanthophore pigments.

Radio Telemetry: tracking activities of organisms by radio signals.

Recessive Gene: an allele that can determine the phenotype only when in homozygous state.

Salamander: general term for tailed amphibian.

Sex Chromosome: special sex-determining chromosome.

Sex-linked: genetic traits determined by genes carried on a sex chromosome.

Sexual Dimorphism: gender differences in characteristics.

Siblings: two or more offspring of the same parents.

Somatic Cells: all cells in an organism aside from the germ cells.

Species: group of organisms which interbreed and are reproductively isolated from all other such groups.

Stem Cell: undifferentiated cell.

Subspecies: well-defined geographic or physiologic aggregate of local population which differs from other such subdivisions of the same species.

Sympatric: having overlapping or coinciding ranges.

Systematics: the classification of organisms in a system to indicate natural relationships.

Taxonomy: scientific naming of organisms and their classification with reference to their precise position in the plant or animal kingdom.

Terrapin: any of a number of fresh water turtles, noted for basking.

Terrestrial: living on ground.

Thermoregulation: in cold-blooded animals, activity associated with external control of body temperature, such as sunning.

Tortoise: common term for some completely terrestrial turtles.

Toxic: poisonous or pertaining to poison.

Tyrosinase: the enzyme essential in synthesis of melanin.

Tyrosinase-negative Albinism: albinism due to absence of tyrosinase.

Tyrosinase-positive Albinism: albinism in animals capable of synthesizing tyrosinase, but yet unable to synthesize melanin.

Tyrosine: the amino acid precursor of melanin, thyroxine, and adrenalin.

Ultraviolet: radiation wavelengths just beyond the violet in the visible spectrum.

Unilateral: found only on one side.

Variant: differing from normal.

Ventral: pertaining to the under or lower surface (venter).

Vertebrate: organism having spinal or vertebral column.

Wild Type: the phenotype occurring normally or with the greatest frequency in a population.

Xanthic: yellowish.

Xanthophore: pigment cell synthesizing red, yellow, and intermediate pteridine pigments.

1
Reptiles and Amphibians

Reptiles and amphibians are cold-blooded (ectothermic or poikilothermic) vertebrates, meaning that they have no internal means of heat regulation. Since they basically depend on heat from the sun to sustain their metabolic processes, warmer climates support the greatest diversity of species. Even with this handicap, they are a remarkably diverse and successful group of animals. Over 6500 species of reptiles have been described, and over 4000 species of amphibians. One or more species of reptiles or amphibians can be found on every continent except Antarctica. Within these geographic areas, they have occupied virtually every habitat niche from deserts to rain forests and from below sea level to high altitudes, and totally aquatic forms have also evolved.

REPTILES

Turtles and Tortoises

More than 240 known species occur in the temperate and tropical regions of all continents except Antarctica, and sea turtles populate every ocean. All turtles are rightly called turtles, but fresh water aquatic forms are often called terrapins, and completely terrestrial varieties are called tortoises.

The feature that makes a turtle a turtle is the shell. The shell is divided into a carapace on top and a plastron on the bottom. The limbs can be withdrawn into the shell when danger threatens.

The shell of the eastern box turtle (*Terrapene c. carolina*) is well suited for protection. The forepart and hindpart of the plastron are hinged so that the turtle can seal itself in when the limbs are withdrawn. The fit is so perfect in most specimens that even a knife blade cannot be inserted between the two shells, and a fox or other predator can worry the turtle at will without being able to harm it. Eastern box turtles are found in suitable areas from southern New Hampshire and Michigan south into Mississippi and Georgia. Most are marked with black, yellow, or orange, with various colors predominating. Some have attractive yellow and reddish spots on the head. They have a high dome-shaped carapace and average 11–15 cm (4½–6 in).

Box turtles are the familiar land turtle through most of their range and are often kept as pets. Will, an ornate box turtle (*Terrapene ornata*) that we collected in Willis Slough in northern Indiana in 1957, had the run of our home for over 30 years before he died. Ornate box turtles are residents of the plains from Indiana west into Wyoming and south through Texas. They are similar to the eastern box turtle, but slightly smaller. Turtles are more intelligent than most reptiles. We never had to remember to feed Will. When he was hungry he would come to the kitchen and remind Bette by crawling back and forth over her feet, and he learned to clamber into the dog's water bowl when thirsty, to the consternation of the dogs. He outlived two of them. All box turtles are omnivorous and easy to cater to, feeding on berries, fruit, raw hamburger, mealworms, and other insects.

A lack of agility is often a trade-off for protection provided by a shell. Shell size is reduced in some of the more agile and aggressive species, and some aquatic species have even evolved non-rigid leathery shells.

Most people are familiar with snapping turtles (*Chelydra serpentina ssp*), if only as the contents of turtle soup. Snapping turtles are common in almost any permanent body of water in the United States east of the Rockies, and large numbers are collected for soups and stews. They average 20–30 cm (8–12 in) with a record of 47 cm (18½ in). They are black to a dirty brown, have a large head, a small plastron, and a long saw-toothed tail. They are aquatic and excellent swimmers, feeding on both plants and animals. Large specimens have even been known to pull a small bird under. Unencumbered by a large heavy shell, snapping turtles are quick and malicious when encountered out of water, striking repeatedly and even lunging. Their bite can be painful, and they should be treated with respect. The proper way to carry one is by the tail, and held away from the body, but large specimens are too heavy to carry this way.

Of all reptiles, turtles enjoy the best relationship with man. None are venomous, and most of them are inoffensive. However, many of the edible species have been overexploited, and loss of habitat to development and other human activity affects them as it does all wildlife.

In south Georgia, a turtle of special concern to all naturalists is the gopher tortoise (*Gopherus polyphemus*). Gopher tortoises inhabit sandy areas of the southeastern coastal plain from extreme eastern Louisiana to the southeast tip of South Carolina, including Florida and southern Mississippi, Alabama, and Georgia. They have a broad flattened dark brown carapace, short stumpy front feet adapted for digging, and elephant-like hind legs. They are large. Adults average 15–25 cm (6–9½ in). In spite of their size, gopher tortoises are completely harmless and so inoffensive that I do not believe it is possible to provoke one into biting. They dig sloping burrows as long as 10 m (35 ft), where they spend their time during winter and when not out foraging for grass, leaves, and berries. These burrows furnish permanent and temporary refuge for an entire community of other reptiles, amphibians, birds, mammals, and insects. Because of its importance to all of these other animals of the sandhill community, gopher tortoises are an indicator species. Where colonies of gopher tortoises thrive, the other animals also thrive. Unfortunately, the sandy areas lend themselves to commercial development and tree farms, gopher tortoise habitat is disappearing rapidly, and these splendid animals are in decline in all parts of their range.

All turtles reproduce by internal fertilization. Eggs are laid on land and depend on ambient temperatures for incubation. In some species, sex is determined by incubation temperatures. The sea turtles spend their lives in the ocean, coming to shore only to lay eggs. They lay their eggs at predictable places and times and are especially vulnerable to exploitation. Enormous numbers of eggs are collected for human food, and adults are hunted relentlessly for their meat. Most species are threatened, endangered, or actually vanishing, but a growing number of enlightened governments have begun to protect nesting beaches.

Terrestrial turtles are herbivorous as a rule, and aquatic forms are often carnivorous or will eat both plant and animal matter. In any event, turtles have no teeth. Hard sharp keratinous jaw sheaths covering both upper and lower jaws replace teeth for biting and tearing food apart. These are sharp in carnivorous species, and the edges are serrated in plant-eating species.

Turtles, particularly tortoises, are believed to be the longest-lived creatures on earth. People occasionally carve the date in the plastron of a box turtle before releasing it, so that the next person who finds it may know how long it has lived. Since box turtles often spend their entire lives in a small range, they may be discovered repeatedly by generations of the same family. On the basis of these records, box turtles can live for more than a century.

Lizards

Over 3500 species of lizards have been described, from all continents except Antarctica and the Arctic. They are exceedingly diverse in habitat preference. Terrestrial, burrowing, tree-dwelling, and semiaquatic species occur.

Lizards typically are scaled and possess four legs and a long tail, but legless species also occur. These are often confused with snakes, but lizards have movable eyelids (with some exceptions) and external ear openings, and snakes do not. They reproduce by internal fertilization. Most lay their eggs on land, but a few give birth to living young. Most lizards will bite when picked up, but all are nonpoisonous except lizards of the genus *Heloderma*, the Gila monster and beaded lizard of the southwestern United States and Mexico.

The largest lizard is the Komodo dragon (*Varanus komodoensis*) of Komodo Island and several other small nearby islands in the East Indies. Adult Komodo dragons average 1.5–1.8 m (4–5 ft), and the largest recorded specimen was an impressive 3.13 m (10 ft 2½ in). Other lizards of this genus, lumped under the general name of monitors, are found in Africa, southern Asia, and Australia, where they are common. All monitors are generally similar in appearance, differing only in size. They have a long neck, long tail, narrow head, and a long deeply forked tongue. All of them are aggressive carnivorous predators. Large Komodo dragons can kill large mammals, and have even caused human fatalities. Their large size and fearsome reputation have made them a tourist attraction. Because of this and their limited range and numbers, they are protected by the Indonesian government.

Lizards as a group have been very successful in occupying many niches because of their many specialized adaptations. Most are noted for their agility, but some have evolved other means of survival.

Many geckos (family, Geckonidae) are not only agile; they have specialized toe pads and have an amazing ability to walk on the ceiling. Geckos are commonly associated with the tropics, and American and European tourists who have never heard of them are often astonished to see a lizard scampering across the ceiling chasing insects. Over 800 species of this large family are distributed across Australia, Africa, South America, and the warmer portions of Europe and North America. Geckos are noted for their various vocalizations, ranging from indistinct chirps to loud barks. Unlike other lizards, most have no movable eyelids.

The tail of many lizards is easily broken off (autotomy) when the lizard is attacked by predators. The broken-off tail wriggles and keeps the attention of the predator while the lizard scurries off to safety. The tail soon regenerates, but the regenerated tail is rarely as perfectly formed as the original.

Glass lizards, or glass snakes as they are often called, are legless lizards noted for the fact that their tails are especially easy to break off. Several similar-appearing but distinct species of these interesting lizards occur in the eastern United States. Though they are confused with snakes by many people, they lack the suppleness of snakes and have a stiff feel, and they tend to lunge rather than crawl gracefully when trying to escape.

The one I see most frequently in south Georgia is the eastern glass lizard (*Ophisaurus ventralis*). Eastern glass lizards range from North Carolina to south Florida and west into Louisiana, with isolated records in Oklahoma and Missouri. Adult eastern glass lizards average 46–108.3 cm (18–42⅝ in). Young specimens are striped and easily confused with other species, but adults are generally an attractive metallic green with bright yellow underside. They are burrowing and secretive, spending much of their time underground, and are primarily insect eaters. As with the other glass lizards, the tail is more than two times the length of the body, and so fragile that it requires care to capture one without the tail accidentally breaking off. Furthermore, if the severed tail is struck, it often breaks into several pieces, giving the appearance that the lizard has shattered like broken glass.

Many lizards can change colors, and the most widely-known for this are the true chameleons (family Chameleonidae). As remarkable as this is, their tongues are equally fantastic. Chameleons are insect eaters, capturing their prey by an adhesive tip on the end of their tongue. The tongue is controlled by a complex musculature that enables it to be projected a distance equal to the head body length of the lizard. When feeding, chameleons judge the distance of an insect, project the tip of the tongue exactly on target, and draw the insect back into the mouth.

Snakes

Over 2300 species of snakes occur worldwide except in the Arctic and Antarctic regions, and in every ocean except the Atlantic. All have a long scaly flexible legless body and lack eyelids and external ear openings. Terrestrial, burrowing, aquatic, marine, and tree-dwelling forms occur.

The relationship between snakes and man is complex, and filled with myths, ignorance, misunderstanding, and unnecessary fear and hatred on the part of man. For the most part, from the standpoint of snakes, the relationship is not a happy one. In all cultures, the relationship is tainted by the fact that many snakes are venomous.

In Christian cultures, the Bible was the original cause for the enmity between snakes and man. The Biblical basis is found in the Book of Genesis:

> But of the fruit of the tree which is in the midst of the garden, God hath said, Ye shall not eat of it, neither shall ye touch it, lest ye die. . . . For God doth know that in the day ye eat thereof, then your eyes shall be opened, and ye shall be as gods, knowing good from evil. . . . And the Lord God said unto the woman, What is this that thou hast done? And the woman said, The serpent beguiled me, and I did eat. And the Lord God said unto the serpent, Because thou has done this, thou are cursed above all cattle, and above every beast in the field; upon thy belly thou shalt go, and dust shalt thou eat all the days of thy life: And I will put enmity between thee and the woman, and between thy seed and her seed; it shall bruise thy head, and thou shalt bruise his heel.

For great numbers of people, this is still a common excuse for killing all snakes on sight. Unfortunately, it is all too true that many snakes are venomous. Interaction between snakes and man is unavoidable, and the bites of some are potentially fatal. With no legs, snakes have evolved strategies for overpowering prey, and envenomation is one of these adaptations. The venom is produced by glands located in the temporal region of the upper jaw. In most poisonous snakes, these glands are associated with fangs (teeth modified for injection of venom). The fangs of vipers are movable and kept folded against the roof of the mouth except when swung forward for striking. The Gaboon viper (*Bitis gabonica*) of Africa has the dubious distinction of possessing the longest fangs, up to 5.8 cm (2 in) in a large specimen. Cobras and a number of other snakes have smaller fixed fangs at the front end of the mouth, while still other snakes are rear-fanged.

Venoms are a complex of toxic substances such as neurotoxic peptides capable of blocking transmission of nerve impulses, tissue-digesting proteases that destroy cell membranes, and hemolytic factors. In general the venom of cobras and other snake eating species is largely neurotoxic, while the venom of vipers and snakes that eat warm-blooded prey consists largely of hemotoxic and proteolytic factors.

A few people learn how to identify the poisonous snakes and avoid them. Many other people cannot, or do not even try to learn to identify them, in spite of the ready availability of excellent guides. They generally go through life with an unwarranted fear of all snakes, and never really give themselves a chance to appreciate these interesting animals. Far too many people still kill all snakes on sight, either to be on the safe side or simply because they do not like snakes.

Though snakes are legless, vestiges of hind limbs are found in four primitive snake families. The boids (pythons and boas) have not only a pelvic girdle, but also rudimentary limbs which manifest themselves as spurs on either side of the vent, more pronounced in males than in females. These have no function in locomotion, but possibly serve some function in sexual activity.

The forked tongue plays a very important role in the life of a snake. It is a specialized neuromuscular organ in no way similar to our tongue other than the fact that it is in the mouth. It is an organ of smell. Snakes as a group depend heavily upon olfaction for such things as finding food, sex identification, and tracking other snakes and prey, and the tongue plays a vital role in the life of the snake. Reptiles are the lowest vertebrates to have twelve cranial nerves, and possess well-developed Jacobson's organs in addition to olfactory nerves. The organs of Jacobson (also called vomeronasal organs) are paired separate blind pouches which open into the roof of the oral cavity. The protrusible tongue is an accessory olfactory organ which picks up minuscule particles from the environment and inserts them into these pouches. The forebrain of the snake has accessory olfactory lobes for receiving impulses from the Jacobson's organs. The result is an exquisite sense of smell. Snakes can seek out prey in dark animal burrows. Males, seeking mates, use olfaction to detect pheromones, the faint odors given off by females. With the flashing tongue, the snake is constantly sampling the environment, and the introduction of any new odor results in very noticeable increased exploratory activity of the tongue.

All snakes reproduce by internal fertilization. Most species lay eggs, but many bear living young. A few species attend the eggs, but no young receive parental care. All snakes are carnivorous and swallow their prey whole. Venom and constriction are two specialized means of killing prey.

Worm Lizards

Worm lizards are burrowing reptiles, specialized for digging. About 140 species can be found on the Iberian Peninsula and nearby north Africa, Arabia and adjacent parts of Asia, South America, sub-Saharan Africa, and Florida.

They are snake-like reptiles with rings of scales encircling the body and tail, and are generally not as well-known as other reptiles. Most of them are 35 cm (14 in) or smaller. Reproduction is by internal fertilization. Some lay eggs, and in others the young develop inside the female's oviducts. They have no external ear openings, and some species even lack eyes.

The Florida worm lizard (*Rhineura floridana*) is the sole American representative. The range is limited to peninsular Florida. Adults average 18–28 cm (7–11 in), with a record 40.6 cm (16 in), are pinkish, and resemble a large earthworm in both form and color. In fact most people who come across worm lizards while working in the yard confuse them with earthworms. They remain beneath the surface, where they feed on small worms and other invertebrates, and are rarely seen except when accidentally dug up or forced to the surface by heavy rains. They reproduce by laying eggs.

Tuatara

Tuataras (*Sphenodon punctatum*) are the only living members of a reptilian order that arose about 220 million years ago. They have survived in much the same form that existed then. Originally, they occupied much of New Zealand, but habitat destruction, introduction of rats and other exotic animals, and other factors exterminated most of them. Remaining colonies survive on a few small islands off the coast of New Zealand, where they are protected by the government.

Superficially, tuataras look like medium-sized lizards with a spiny crest the length of the body and tail, but they differ from true lizards in several ways. They lack external ear openings, and they are noted for their third eye. Lizards have a form of third eye on the top of the head, where the cranium is perforated to allow nervous processes from the brain to contact a light-sensitive transparent disk on the top of the head. This is not used for vision, but may be involved in the biological clock. The third eye of the tuatara is much more fully developed, complete with lens, retina, and nervous connections to the brain. It is sensitive to light, but there is no evidence that it is used for vision. It gets covered over with thickened skin as the tuatara ages. Tuataras also have a third eyelid that sweeps across the eye while the two conventional eyelids are open.

Crocodilians

The 22 crocodilian species include 7 alligator species, 14 crocodile species, and the gharial. All are readily recognized as crocodilians, but there are differences.

Alligators are found in North and South America and China. The American representative is the American alligator (*Alligator mississippiensis*).

Crocodiles are native to North and South America, Africa, India and Southeast Asia, and Australia. The American crocodile (*Crocodylus acutus*) is limited to the Greater Antilles, southern Mexico to Columbia and Ecuador, plus a limited range in south Florida and the Keys. In south Florida, where the range overlaps that of the alligator, questions are constantly asked how to tell them apart, since they are superficially very similar. Alligators have a broadly rounded snout with no conspicuous teeth in the lower jaw. Crocodiles have a tapering snout with the fourth lower jaw teeth protruding upward near the snout.

The gharial differs in appearance from the other crocodilians by having a greatly elongated snout. The snout of the males has a pot-like tip. Found only on the Indian subcontinent, the sole species in the family (*Gavialis gangeticus*) is nearly extinct.

Crocodilians are aquatic and carnivorous. All reproduce by internal fertilization, and all lay eggs. The nests and eggs are guarded by the female, and some species care for the young for a year or more after hatching. As a group, males are larger than females.

AMPHIBIANS

Over 4000 species of amphibians have been described. Most of them live part of their life in water and part on land. The word amphibian is taken from the Greek word *amphibios* (living a double life). Terrestrial and aquatic forms also occur. Amphibians are divided into caecilians, salamanders and newts, and frogs and toads.

Caecilians

For most herpetologists, caecilians are the least known of the amphibians, even though over 150 species occupy suitable habitat in Central and South America, Africa, the Asian subcontinent, and Southeast Asia. One species is aquatic, while the others inhabit loose soil and ground litter near water. Essentially burrowers, most of them have small, generally functionless eyes. There are small movable feelers or tentacles sprouting from a groove on each side of the snout between the eye and the nostril. These feelers are most likely organs of smell. Caecilians have sharp teeth, and feed on invertebrates, but most of them are unable to harm anything aside from the grubs they feed on.

Caecilians are limbless and segmentally ringed, looking like earthworms. Various species range from about 12.7 cm (5 in) to about 120 cm (4 ft). All caecilians are nonpoisonous. They reproduce by internal fertilization. Some lay eggs near the water and the larvae enter water and become land-dwelling after metamorphosis. Hatchlings have frilly external scarlet gills, but these are transient. Some species undergo metamorphosis within the eggs and hatch as miniature adults, while in others the young are retained in the oviducts through metamorphosis and are born alive.

Salamanders and Newts

Over 350 species of salamanders and newts occur in North and South America, Europe, Africa, and Asia, encompassing aquatic, amphibious, and terrestrial varieties. Most of the terrestrial forms prefer moist cool situations, since all salamanders need moisture.

Most salamanders and newts are built like lizards, and are often confused with lizards. In parts of the country where they are used for fish bait, they are often called spring lizards. However, salamanders have smooth or warty skin and are clawless, while lizards are scaled and have claws.

The largest American salamander is the hellbender (*Cryptobranchus allega-niensis*), a big aquatic salamander found in the Susquehanna River drainage of eastern Pennsylvania and west into Illinois and south into northern Alabama. A related subspecies, similar in appearance and habits, is found in several limited river drainages in Missouri and Arkansas. Most people describe hellbenders as ugly or grotesque, which is true. They spend their life in water, feeding on crayfish, earthworms, and other vertebrates and invertebrates. They have a large flattened head and are covered with loose wrinkled folds of brownish or grayish skin. They are harmless, though many people still think they are poisonous and are afraid of them. Slimy is an adjective often applied to amphibians, and even some reptiles, by people who have never tried to hold onto a hellbender. Even herpetologists call them slimy. They average 29–51 cm (11½–20 in), with a record 68.6 cm (29⅛ in). To give an idea of their size, most American salamanders and newts are less than ⅓ as long.

Some salamanders are legless or nearly so. The two-toed amphiuma (*Amphiuma means*) of the coastal plain of the southeastern United States is an example. The range extends from southern Virginia through Florida and west into Louisiana. Two-toed amphiumas are black or brown eel-like salamanders with two pairs of tiny useless-looking legs. They average 46–76 cm (18–30 in), but have been recorded as long as 116.2 cm (45¾ in). These large salamanders inhabit ditches, ponds, swamps, and sloughs, where they forage for invertebrates and even small vertebrates. No salamanders or newts are venomous, and most do not even try to bite, but amphiumas can and do bite. I got my hands on a large one before I knew that they could bite, and sustained a severe laceration of the palm, which turned out to be the worst bite I ever received from any nonpoisonous reptile or amphibian.

Some salamanders, like many lizards, have the ability to grow a new tail if the original one is lost. Even more remarkable is the ability to regenerate an entire new limb. I learned this when two tiger salamanders (*Ambystoma tigrinum*) that I had in a terrarium got into a fight and one had an entire front limb torn off. Some time later I noticed a small new limb growing. The salamander eventually grew a new replacement, including all toes. This potential has intrigued scientists for years, who would like to make the same regeneration available to the human race. Needless to say, the secret is still locked in the salamander.

Frogs and Toads

Frogs and toads are tailless amphibians. referred to collectively as anurans. Most people around Valdosta, Georgia refer to toads as toad-frogs. I never heard them called this until I moved to Georgia from Pennsylvania, and 30 years later I am still not accustomed to it. While there is no purely scientific objection to this terminology, there are differences between toads and frogs. Frogs are smooth skinned, often have long legs, and most of them live in water. Toads have warty skin, have short legs, and generally live in moist situations away from water. Having said this, there are no hard and fast rules for telling one from the other.

So many species exist, and they are so diverse that it is difficult to generalize about them. Over 3400 species have been described, and they are found on all continents except Antarctica. Terrestrial, amphibious, and aquatic forms occur, and one or more species occupies nearly every type of habitat in their broad range. They differ from other amphibians by the absence of a tail in their adult stage and by their long hind legs adapted for jumping, or hopping in the case of toads. They are visually oriented and most species have prominent eyes. Some are remarkably patterned with brilliant colors, and some are inconspicuous brown shades. Most range from 2–12 cm (.8–4.8 in), and none is larger than 35 cm (14 in).

Herpetologists' adrenalin begins to flow in early spring when they hear the trills, barks, grunts, snores, peeps, bleats, whistles, and other sounds in roadside ditches and other bodies of water. These seemingly random noises are the calls of male frogs and toads trying to attract mates. The calls are highly species-specific, and frogs' ears tend to be tuned to the frequency levels of calls of their own species. This prevents hybridization. Herpetologists also use these calls to identify species. When listening to a loud chorus of different calls, all competing for the attention of female frogs, it is generally possible to identify which frogs are in the pond.

Fertilization is external. When a male finds a female at breeding season he clasps her and clings to her back in a grip called amplexus. During amplexus, fertilization takes place as the eggs are extruded from the female.

The fertilized eggs of frogs and toads hatch into tadpoles. Children collect tadpoles in order to observe the remarkable phenomenon called metamorphosis. The eggs hatch into short plump-bodied tadpoles with long vertically flattened tails. Tadpoles of different frog and toad species differ in size and other characters, but only an expert can identify many of them. They are vegetarians, even those that metamorphose into carnivorous adults.

Tadpoles typically hatch with external gills, but are shortly breathing with internal gills. The tadpole stage lasts from a few days to several years in some species. In the metamorphosis of a tadpole to a frog, the hind legs appear first, followed by the appearance of front legs. By the time the internal gills are replaced by lungs, the tail has shrunk to a stump, and the frog hops away from the water.

2
Biology of the Skin

SNAKES

Anatomy

The skin is a protective covering of overlapping scales serving various functions. Most species possess large symmetrically arranged head scales, small dorsal body scales, and enlarged undivided ventral plates corresponding more or less with the number of vertebrae. Their number, arrangement, relative size, and morphology are species specific and determined genetically. Scales are used as recognition characters by taxonomists. Since scutellation is less variable than color pattern, it may be the sole method for identifying a snake, such as one that has faded in preservative fluid. Counting scales and checking for presence or absence of scales are important in snake systematics.

The scales of some species are smooth, while other snake species have a longitudinal keel or ridge on all or most scales. Snakes with smooth scales, such as kingsnakes of the genus *Lampropeltis*, are shiny and waxen in appearance. The word lampropeltis is derived from *lampros*, Greek for brilliant, and *pellis*, Latin for skin. Snakes with small keels, often involving only a few body scales, are also often lustrous, but those with conspicuous keels, such as watersnakes of the genus *Nerodia*, are frequently dull or even velvety in appearance. The presence or absence of keels may be useful in snake identification since their presence is determined genetically. In most snakes, the skin between the scales is visible only when it is distended or stretched, as it is after a large meal.

In common with the skin of other vertebrates, snake skin consists of an outer superficial epidermis and an underlying dermis. Epidermis and dermis have separate origins. Immediately after fertilization, the egg begins to subdivide through a series of mitotic divisions into numerous cells which will be building blocks for the future organism. The new cells position themselves into three superimposed primary germ layers: the outer ectoderm, a middle mesoderm, and the inner endoderm. The germ layers continue to divide and gradually differentiate into tissues, which in turn become organs. Epidermis, skin glands, and the nervous system arise from the ectoderm. The embryonic mesoderm differentiates into dermis, muscle, skeleton, circulatory system, gonads, kidneys, and respiratory tract. The liver, pancreas, and linings of the digestive and respiratory tracts arise from the embryonic endoderm.

The epidermis is composed of living layers of cells called keratinocytes, with an overlying stratum corneum. The epidermis is avascular. The basal layer of keratinocytes, resting on the upper dermis, proliferate throughout the snake's life and either migrate to the skin surface, or are forced upward by the formation of new cells. As they approach the surface, they transform into keratin. Epidermal melanophores are found scattered among the basal cells.

The stratum corneum is composed of a tough fibrous protein consisting essentially of dead keratinocytes (keratin). The orderly transformation of the metabolically active cytoplasm in the basal epidermal cells into the horny dead keratin layer as the cells migrate upward is known as keratinization. This process involves water loss and concentration of the cytoplasmic contents of the keratinocytes.

The dermis is composed largely of connective tissue fibers with scattered fibroblasts and capillaries. The connective tissue fibers are loosely arranged in a gelatinous ground substance in most of the dermis, but more compact in the zone immediately adjacent to the epidermis and in the deep dermis. The dermis forms a substrate for cutaneous blood vessels, chromatophores, and pain and temperature receptors.

Scales are not composed exclusively of keratin. They are overlapping folds of skin, and each scale contains dermis and all layers of the epidermis. The stratum corneum is relatively thick on the exposed crawling surfaces.

Shedding

The periodic shedding of skin by snakes is remarkable, and seems to fascinate those who are not familiar with the ways of snakes. In an indirect way, it is even responsible for the fact that a snake on a staff (the caduceus) is the symbol of the medical profession. From ancient times, serpents have been associated with fertility and healing. In many cultures, they were worshiped and associated with healing because they were thought to possess the secret of eternal youth. This belief undoubtedly has its roots in the observable phenomenon of the snake sloughing its skin and assuming a second life. It is man's belief in the serpent as a healer that is in the background of the caduceus.

To be precise, snakes do not shed their skin. In most animals, in the course of normal wear and tear, keratin is rubbed off and shed continuously, and generally inconspicuously. Snakes have an unusually thick and tough keratin layer, adapted to their legless life style, and they periodically shed (molt) the entire keratin layer, including the transparent eye caps, in one piece in a process called ecdysis.

Shortly before ecdysis, lymph diffuses between the thick keratin layer and the underlying epidermis, the colors of the snake become less intense, and the eyes become blue and semiopaque. A day or two before the actual shed, the snake's colors resume a nearly normal brightness and the eyes become clear. Shedding is generally initiated at the head region by a mechanism which increases the venous pressure in the head, and actually results in an enlargement of the head due to this vascular engorgement. Thus, it takes a minimum of rubbing and traction to initiate the shedding process at the lips. After the skin pulls away from the lips and is pulled back over the head, the snake slowly crawls out, leaving the skin as a translucent inside-out replica of itself, showing every scale. Within a few days following shedding, a burst of cell multiplication takes place in the basal layer of the epidermis, the new cells begin to migrate upwards and keratinize, and the entire process begins again.

Quite frequently, homeowners do not even suspect that a snake lives in their yard until they come upon a cast skin stretched among the shrubs. They have even been known to mistake the cast for the snake itself and call me to identify it. Because the number and arrangement of the scales are species specific it is often possible to identify the snake by the cast, or even a fragment of it.

The frequency of shedding is influenced by factors such as species, nutrition, climate, and age. Several other factors influence frequency or timing of shedding. Injured snakes, or snakes with diseases involving the skin, shed with abnormal frequency until the skin is healed. For reasons not entirely understood, pregnant snakes have a prepartum shed shortly before eggs are laid. This is apparently not related to the normal shedding cycle, and occurs at a fixed number of days before egg-laying. The timing of the prepartum shed differs with species. Young snakes shed shortly after they are born or hatched. Snakes generally refuse food during the days and even weeks preceding shedding.

Snakes shed the delicate sheath from the tips of the tongue frequently. This does not appear to be synchronized with the casting cycle in general.

Function

Skin functions as a protective barrier against wear and tear, and injury to internal organs. Keratin is the first line of defense for snakes, whose bodies are in continuous contact with sand, gravel, stones, sharp objects, and even soil pollutants. Their unusually thick stratum corneum is especially adapted for this.

The less obvious function is as a physiological barrier. The skin prevents toxic substances from diffusing into the snake from the environment. As important as this is, the major function is the conservation of body fluids and prevention of dehydration. The physiological barrier is not absolute, however, since there is some cutaneous oxygen intake in all snakes, and considerable uptake in sea snakes. Immature snakes are more subject to dehydration.

By virtue of melanin, skin protects the organism from harmful effects of ultraviolet radiation. Melanin also plays a role in thermoregulation. All of the pigment cells have a role in production of color pattern.

Scale Modifications and Appendages

Skin and scale modifications in various snakes include facial pits in pit vipers, labial pits in pythons and some boas, cloacal glands, paravertebral glands, horns on the nose of a number of species, projections over the eyes of some, fleshy protrusions, and sharp horny tails.

The facial pits of pit vipers and the labial pits of the large boids are heat sensors, and pit vipers are named because of these pits. The facial pits of pit vipers are located on the sides of the face between the eyes and nostrils, while most boas and pythons possess similar pits on the lips. These organs are extremely sensitive to infrared heat rays and can detect temperature differences as little as 1° C higher or lower than that of the background, which is important to snakes that feed on warm-blooded animals. When a pit viper is tracking an animal in a burrow, it can direct an accurate strike in the dark. It has long been a routine at snake shows to place a balloon filled with warm air in front of a rattlesnake to demonstrate that it strikes towards heat. In most of the demonstrations that I have seen, the snake was so aroused and tormented that it was ready to strike at any object, hot or cold, or else so worn out with tormenting that it did not want to strike at anything.

The sidewinder (*Crotalus cerastes*) is known for the peculiar modification of the supraorbital scales (over the eyes). Sidewinders are small desert dwelling rattlesnakes, native to the desert and arid areas from southern Nevada and Utah south through western Arizona and southern California into Mexico and Baja California. In addition to small mammals, they feed on lizards and even insects. They are less than 91.5 cm (36 in) long, and patterned with indistinct blotches, often just mottling, against a gray or tan background that matches the arid desert habitat. The name sidewinder is derived from a looping way of locomotion in which the snake appears to be facing one way and moving another. Sidewinding allows rapid locomotion on soft sand, avoiding unnecessary contact with the heat. The snakes are nocturnal and remain buried in the sand or rodent burrows during the day.

Sidewinders are often called horned rattlesnakes because the hornlike supra-orbital scales are pointed upward. These scales are soft and fold down completely covering the eyes when the snakes are hunting in tight dark rodent burrows where vision is not needed. Between their rattle, horns, and peculiar mode of crawling, sidewinders have a reputation and recognition out of proportion to their size and importance. Most of the other southwestern rattlesnakes are more of a threat to man.

The few glands that are present in snakes are useful for warding off predators, species and sex recognition, and courtship. Chin rubbing is a common courtship activity among snakes, and the paired chain of paravertebral glands in natricine snakes and some related species possibly function in this way. Certainly chin rubbing would bring the nose into proximity with the glands. Rapid tongue flicking is also part of the courtship activity, indicating that the snakes are trying to pick up odors.

The rattle of rattlesnakes is the one modification almost everyone knows about. Rattlesnakes are unique to the Americas. They fascinated the first European settlers, they have fascinated everyone since then, and they fascinate me. When a south Georgian kills a rattlesnake, he almost always brags about the number of rattles (segments) it had, even before he tells me how long the snake was. Speculation regarding the function of the rattle has persisted to the present, but it is generally agreed that the rattle is a warning intended to protect the snake from any threat to itself. Whatever the function, snakes evidently use their rattles infrequently. A new segment is added each time the snake casts. Since rattlesnakes cast one or more times per year, their age cannot be determined by the number of segments. The number of times a snake casts is influenced by nutrition, duration of warm weather and snake activity, by species differences, and other factors.

In the field, I am most familiar with the timber rattlesnake (*Crotalus horridus*), because it was the common rattlesnake near Johnstown, Pennsylvania, where I lived when I first became interested in snakes, and it was the first poisonous snake I found. The range extends from Massachusetts south into Florida and west into Wisconsin and Texas. They have been exterminated in many parts of their original range, and the remaining populations are under increasing pressure from human activities. This handsome snake has two color phases, yellow and black. Yellow phased snakes have a yellow, brown, or gray background color with irregular black or brown crossbands. There is considerable individual variation in quantity and quality of the colors. Most of the black rattlesnakes have some trace of pattern still visible. The southern coastal plain variants are gray or pinkish with a reddish mid-dorsal stripe dividing the crossbands. They average 91–137 cm (36–54 in), with a record of 188 cm (74 in). They feed on chipmunks and other small mammals, as well as birds, and are sit-and-wait predators, lying coiled up and motionless for long periods waiting for prey. In the north, they congregate in dens in rocky hillsides during the winter.

In all of my tramping about in the mountains of western Pennsylvania, on only one occasion has a snake rattled without being specifically prodded or physically touched by me. I was walking along a dirt road on a hot summer day when a large yellow phase timber rattlesnake suddenly rattled. It was well off to the side of the road hidden in a thicket of huckleberry bushes, and I would never have seen the snake if it had not called attention to itself by rattling. I have never heard one rattling somewhere off in the woods, and without doubt have nearly stepped on more than one without knowing it.

OTHER REPTILES

The principles of skin embryology, anatomy, and function of the other reptiles are similar to those of snakes. Their skin consists of dermis and epidermis. Many of the specializations in snake skin are evolved to accommodate a legless existence, and some to accommodate an ectothermal metabolism. Turtles, crocodilians, and lizards are also cold-blooded. However, with the exception of a few lizards, they possess legs, and differ from snakes in other ways.

Lizards, as a group, have more scales that are specialized into spines, crests, and other configurations. Spines of lizards generally consist of single enlarged scales with sharp points. The spines are often arranged in crests on the neck or over the backbone. In some lizards the most prominent spines are on the tail. In all cases they serve as protection from predators.

In the United States, horned lizards are known for their crest of spiny scales on the back of the head and the row of small spines on the fringes of the sides of the abdomen. Nearly everyone can recognize a horned lizard, and the best known one is the Texas horned lizard or "horned toad" (*Phrynosoma cornutum*), found in Texas and all or parts of every surrounding state, as well as Mexico. Texas horned lizards average 6–10 cm (2½–4 in), and are generally some shade of light brown with rows of conspicuous dark brown dorsal spots. Their general build reminds people of toads, and their short flattened bodies and earth colors blend into the arid situations in which they are most often found. The two central head spines are much longer than the others, and jut upwards as small horns. Horned lizards are diurnal and feed on insects, especially ants, which they pick up with a flick of the tongue. At one time, thousands of these unfortunate little lizards ended up in the tourist trade as live pets or mounted curios, in spite of that fact they rarely survive long in captivity even in the best circumstances. Fortunately, enlightened legislation has brought this practice to a halt, and the greatest threat to horned lizards now is the progressive loss of habitat to development.

Horned lizards possess the remarkable ability to squirt a thin stream of blood from the forward corner of the eye to a distance of several feet. This is made possible by a mechanism that increases blood pressure in the head, and is apparently a last ditch defense mechanism against major predators. When a lizard sprays blood into the mouth or nostrils of a dog, the dog salivates excessively and shows every evidence of distaste, and probably does not torment any more horned lizards. This feat sounds so unbelievable that many people regard it as a myth.

In many lizards, instead of overlapping, the scales are beaded or granular. The Gila monster (*Heloderma suspectum*) is an example. Gila monsters are found in Arizona and nearby portions of California, New Mexico, Nevada, Utah, and Mexico. Gila monsters are heavy-bodied, with a blunt tail, and their dorsal surface is covered with bead-like scales in a showy irregular pattern of black, pink, orange, and yellow. They average 45.7–61 cm (18–24 in). They eat small rodents, birds, lizards, and eggs. The Gila monster and the other member of the genus, the beaded lizard (*Heloderma horridum*) are the only known venomous lizards. Gila monsters have powerful jaws and sharp teeth. When they bite, they hang on, and the experience is painful. However, Gila monsters are not aggressive and nearly all bites are inflicted on people who are handling or tormenting the lizards. Fatalities are all but unknown. The beaded lizard of Mexico is slightly larger than the Gila monster, less colorful, and with more brown or black in the pattern. Their overall appearance is quite similar.

Many groups of lizards have preanal and femoral glands that open into dermal follicles. These pores are usually situated along the back and undersurface of each thigh. They may be present in both sexes, but are usually better developed in males, and are thought to play some role in sexual activity.

All crocodilians possess bony plates in the dermis beneath the enlarged scales on the neck, back, and tail. Turtles have the greatest degree of modification. The scales in most species do not overlap. They form laminae, thin layers covering the underlying dermal bony plates of the plastron and carapace. The shell is an elaborate modification for defense against predators.

Crocodilians possess two pairs of musk glands, one pair on the throat and one in the cloacal opening. Some turtles have musk glands along the edge of the mandible and also in the skin of the axillary and inguinal areas between the plastron and carapace. Odoriferous secretions from these glands have a role in protection or sex recognition.

The egg caruncles of turtles, crocodilians, and the tuatara are epithelial structures that disappear after playing their role in enabling hatchlings to escape from their eggs. The egg tooth of the snake, on the other hand, is actually a true dentine-covered tooth. The upper and lower jaws of turtles are keratinous structures functioning as teeth.

Like snakes, lizards also shed their entire skin at regular intervals. In most species it is shed in random sized sheets and pieces rather than intact. Many species assist the shedding process by tearing away pieces of the skin with their teeth, and often eating it. This strategy recycles valuable protein.

AMPHIBIANS

The basic plan of amphibian skin is modified in all but the caecilians for life in water or a damp environment. Respiration in most vertebrates involves transfer of gases in vascular networks in lungs or gills. Though they have lungs, amphibians also exchange gases through the skin. This is facilitated by a smooth, moist, thin skin. A large family of salamanders (Plethodontidae) are lungless and depend entirely on cutaneous and buccopharyngeal (gas exchange in the lining of the oral and pharyngeal cavity) respiration when adult.

The keratin layer is poorly developed and epidermal scales are absent, except for caecilians. Caecilians have segmental rings, and many have patches of scales in these rings, in which the keratin layer is better developed. Frogs and toads possess keratinous pads or thumbs, which are used in amplexus. The superficial epidermal layer is molted at regular intervals. Depending on the species, molting may be on all surfaces at once or in pieces. As with lizards, some amphibians eat their cast skin.

Tadpoles and some other amphibians possess a lateral line, a row of specialized sensory organs on the sides that are sensitive to water pressure changes. Some aquatic forms retain the lateral line after metamorphosing.

Amphibian integument, unlike that of reptiles, possesses many glands. These are divided into two types: mucous and granular. If the skin is to serve a respiratory function, it must be moist. Mucous glands in the dermis, but of epidermal origin, secrete clear watery mucus which keeps the skin moist when the amphibians are out of water and lubricates the skin when they are in water. Modified mucous glands play a role in sex recognition and also in control of body temperature through evaporation.

The secretions of granular glands contain digitalis-like substances that are distasteful or even toxic. These glands are concentrated in the parotoid glands behind the heads of toads and some frogs, and on the glandular ridges along the backs of salamanders.

Though some poison is present in the skin secretions of all amphibians, it is insignificant in most cases. In some, however, it is sufficiently potent to kill large vertebrates.

The granular secretions of poison arrow frogs (family Dendrobatidae) contain some of the most potent toxins known. This group of tiny frogs inhabits moist tropics of Central and South America. Many are boldly patterned in shades of red, blue, green, and gold, rivaling tropical butterflies in brilliance. The bright colors are probably meant to discourage predators, and predators are well advised to be discouraged. One species is so poisonous that it is unsafe to handle even when the skin of the hands is intact. The indiginous Indians tip their arrows with toxic secretions from these frogs for hunting, and a small amount of poison can kill a large animal. In the past, the technique was even used in warfare.

Toads are also known for toxic skin secretions, particularly the marine toad (*Bufo marinus*). Marine toads are large brown to grayish-brown toads averaging 10–15 cm (4–6 in), with a record specimen of 23.8 cm (9⅜ in). For comparison, the next largest toad in Florida, the southern toad (*Bufo terrestris*), averages 4.1–7.6 cm (1⅝–3 in). They are warty and look like most toads, but are distinguished by large pitted parotoid glands extending down the body beyond the shoulders.

Marine toads were introduced into south Florida from their native habitat in South America to help control insects in the sugar cane fields. They found Florida attractive and have adapted to the suburban south Florida lifestyle, and are now common over a large and expanding area. They are able to squirt toxic secretions from the parotoid glands into eyes and ears of predators, and accounts of dogs and cats becoming ill from trying to eat them are common. There have even been human fatalities when the toad has been introduced into undeveloped countries, where the indigenous people, unaware of their toxicity, tried eating them. They were also introduced into Australia for insect control, where they are even more of a pest than they are in Florida.

When attacked, marine toads bend the head down so as to present the predator with the worst tasting part. A number of toads use this defense, and some species of salamanders with toxic secretions at the back of the head use the same defense.

3
Genetics

```
┌─────────────────────────────────────────────────────┐
│ ┌─────────────────────────────────────────────────┐ │
│ │  INTRODUCTION                                     │ │
│ └─────────────────────────────────────────────────┘ │
└─────────────────────────────────────────────────────┘
```

INTRODUCTION

Genetics is the biology of heredity, particularly individual variation and the mechanism of transmission of hereditary traits. Over 300 million years ago the first primitive four-legged vertebrates evolved from aquatic ancestors. The thousands of reptiles and amphibians that exist today evolved from these precursors. Their colors, patterns, scales, and other morphological features, the characteristics that make them what they are, are determined by their genes.

Many of the remaining chapters of this book deal with abnormal reptiles and amphibians. Just as every feature of every species is determined by the genes, most of the anomalies discussed in the following chapters are also caused by genes. This seeming contradiction is explained by the basic principles of genetics.

Genes not only determine the characteristics of reptiles and amphibians, but genes have determined their evolution. Evolution is the descent of organisms from preexisting life forms through change in the genetic composition of a population from one generation to the next. As a result, genetics and evolution are interrelated to the extent that we cannot explain one without knowledge of the other, and speculation about the two subjects goes back many years. Some controversy persists to the present regarding evolution. Two men have become almost household words due to their contribution to our knowledge of evolution and heredity: Charles Darwin and Gregor Mendel.

Charles Darwin was born in England in 1809. Because of his interest in natural history, at the age of 22 he was recommended for the unpaid position of ship naturalist on the H.M.S. *Beagle*. This was an age of discovery, and the *Beagle* was commissioned by the British government to survey the coasts of South America and nearby islands. Darwin's duties were to study the rocks and life of the places visited and collect specimens. The voyage lasted five years, and included a stop at the Galapagos Islands. While on the *Beagle* voyage, Darwin contracted an illness that his doctors could not diagnose or treat. It is now thought that he had Chagas' disease (South American trypanosomiasis), a chronic illness caused by the protozoan,

Trypanosoma cruzi, and transmitted by a bloodsucking bug. He spent the remainder of his life as a semi-invalid and died in 1882.

The voyage was the turning point in Darwin's life, and resulted in a decisive moment in the science of biology. It took place at a time of active scientific inquiry. The prevailing view that species of plants and animals were created divinely and were immutable was unsatisfactory and openly questioned. The Lamarckan theory that acquired characteristics could be inherited had some adherents in the scientific world, but scientists were searching for other answers. When Darwin set out on the *Beagle*, he had no reason to differ with current views. From observations made on the trip, however, Darwin began to formulate his theories of evolution. He published *On the Origin of Species* in 1859, in which he outlined his theory of natural selection. This theory is based on conclusions inferred from several basic observations.

1. All species produce more young than are needed for a stable population. Therefore, there must be a high mortality rate.
2. Individuals within a species vary, and some variations enable individuals to better deal with the environment and survive and reproduce.
3. At least some of the variation in ability to adapt is due to inheritable differences.
4. Over time, successive generations have an increased proportion of the better adapted traits. Species and races arise by accumulation of significant inherited differences.

Darwin's ideas impacted much traditional thinking and were not accepted by all, and this included scientists as well as theologians. However, his theory of evolution has endured, and many lines of evidence help confirm it. It is the basis for our understanding today. It has subsequently permeated all branches of human thought and is the glue that binds the various biological disciplines.

Darwin did not arrive at his conclusions in a vacuum. Evolution was the subject of much discussion in the early 1800's. Another Englishman, Alfred Russell Wallace, independently arrived at the same conclusions that Darwin did, and at about the same time, but Darwin's is the name associated with evolution in the minds of most people.

The basis of natural selection did not become clear for many years after the theory of evolution was put forward. Gregor Mendel formulated the principles of heredity that explained natural selection and were to become the modern science of genetics.

Gregor Mendel was born in Austria in 1822. He entered a monastery and was ordained a priest. At the University of Vienna he studied mathematics and science, and learned the scientific method. Working in the monastery garden, he decided to find an explanation for the heredity of peas. He began by mating plants of a pure red-flowering strain with those that bore only white flowers. The offspring (F_1, or first filial generation) of this original mating were all red-flowered. However, when he mated any of the red-flowered F_1 plants together, their offspring (F_2, or second filial generation) were in a ratio of three red-flowered to one white-flowered. He eventually came to conclusions now called Mendelian Laws.

1. Inherited characteristics are produced by factors (physical entities).
2. In each individual, these factors are found in pairs, and where the two factors in a pair are different in their effects, one dominates the other.
3. When seeds are formed in any individual, the members of each pair of factors segregate independently. Which member of a pair of factors becomes included in the gamete is chance.

Mendel succeeded where all others before him had failed. Not only was he brilliant, but in his investigations he worked with peas, which are self-fertilizing, concentrated on only one trait at a time, and had the good fortune to work with traits that were not linked. Furthermore, being a mathematician, he counted numbers. His findings were published in 1866, and he died in 1884. The importance of these findings was not appreciated until 1890, partly because he did not follow up on his own work. Subsequent investigations established these laws as the foundation for the science of genetics. Mendel's factors came to be recognized as genes.

Thomas Hunt Morgan, a professor at Columbia University, made major contributions to our understanding of genetics by working with fruit flies (*Drosophila melanogaster*). He proved that genes are parts of chromosomes, and chromosomes carry more than one gene, and he was also the first to explain sex-linkage.

PRINCIPLES

All cells arise from preexisting cells by cell division. Most multicellular animals begin their development as a fertilized egg that contains all inherited instructions for all heritable traits from both parents. Provided with a suitable environment, a fertilized egg then proceeds to differentiate into an organism containing billions of cells. In the case of the endothermic animals and birds, the duration of gestation varies with species. In the case of the ectothermic reptiles and amphibians, gestation and incubation not only vary with species, but duration is affected by temperature.

The fertilized egg begins immediately to subdivide to form a multicellular organism. Each cell of the embryo will not grow or function properly unless it receives the necessary inherited information in the form of parental genes, and genes are now known to be deoxyribonucleic acid (DNA). DNA is composed of subunits called nucleotides, the genetic information of all living cells. DNA consequently contains instructions for building proteins, synthesizing enzymes, and other developmental and physiological requisites. The genes are found in each cell nucleus in linear strands called chromosomes. The chromosomes occur in pairs, one of the pair from the male parent and the other from the female, and each species has a characteristic number of chromosomes.

The chromosomes in each somatic cell (nonsex cell) contain genes for a particular inherited trait. These genes direct all life processes: cell division, cell differentiation, assembly of cells into organs, and assembly of organs into the organism. When any somatic cell divides, the chromosomes make copies of themselves and pass them to the daughter cells. This type of cell division is called mitosis, and each daughter, eventually every living somatic cell in the body, contains the same genetic information that was in the original fertilized egg.

Germ cells in the ovaries and testes are a lineage set aside to produce gametes (sperm and ova) for reproduction. The germ cells contain paired chromosomes identical to those in somatic cells, but the gametes are produced by a form of cell division that reduces the number of chromosomes in the ovum or sperm by ½. A cell with ½ the number of chromosomes is called haploid: therefore sperm and ova are haploid. A cell that contains the normal number of chromosomes is called diploid. The type of cell division that produces haploid cells is called meiosis.

Early in the course of meiosis, besides producing haploid cells, there can be an exchange of corresponding segments of DNA between homologous chromosomes, in a process called crossing over. Since the crossing over is random, the genes in a sperm or ovum from either parent are determined by chance. This allows for variation in the genetic makeup of the offspring. The offspring will have a full complement of all inherited traits: the gene for any one trait that an offspring receives from either parent is determined by chance.

Many offspring resemble their parents because they inherit characteristics from both parents. However, sometimes offspring do not resemble either parent. Both consequences, though seemingly contradictory, are explained by the same laws of genetics. When predicted outcomes of a mating do not seem to conform to Mendelian principles, there has to be an explanation. Though Mendel's laws are true and have been confirmed many times, major advances since then have enabled us to explain these inconsistencies, and advances are still being made.

Any one trait is determined by a pair of homologous genes. These paired genes are referred to as alleles. Any gene may be altered by mutation. A mutation is the result of random fundamental change in the structure of the DNA molecule. Agents that can induce these changes are called mutagens, and include many things: physical factors such as radiation, chemical and toxic substances, and other less common causes. Since any one trait is controlled by a pair of genes, mutation of one gene of the pair goes unnoticed in most cases. When mutations produce an effect, it may be beneficial, harmful, or even lethal. Mutations are the prerequisites for variability and evolution, and each mutation is tested by natural selection. Individuals with beneficial mutations live in greater numbers to sexual maturity, and make up an increasing proportion of the population.

Most mutations happen to somatic cells and are not passed to offspring. If a mutated gene is in a germ cell it may be passed on to offspring, enter the gene pool, and be transmitted to subsequent generations. More than one mutation may occur at a single locus, resulting in multiple alleles in the population, and each allele may code for a different modification of the trait controlled by the pair of genes at that locus. Thus, even though a single individual can have only two alleles for a given trait, multiple alleles may be available in the gene pool for selection at the locus for that trait.

In some forms, one allele is dominant over its paired allele, and can completely mask the expression of its recessive gene. However, a dominant gene does not alter the DNA of the recessive allele, and both are passed unaltered to offspring. Organisms containing two identical copies of the same gene are called homozygous. When the paired alleles are not the same, the organism is heterozygous for that trait.

The combination of genes is called the genotype. The appearance of an organism is called the phenotype, and the phenotype is determined by the genotype. In reproduction, either gene from either parent has an equal chance of showing up in the offspring. Thus, a recessive allele can be carried by both parents with no evidence in their phenotype, but their offspring can be homozygous for the recessive allele and have a phenotype different from either parent.

Chromosomes found in homologous pairs in both males and females and which do not bear the genes determining sex are designated as autosomes. The sex of an individual is determined by sex chromosomes designated x and y. Females have two x chromosomes, and males have one x and one y chromosome. x chromosomes contain some genes with no corresponding gene on the y chromosome. This allows any gene on the unapposed portion of the x chromosome to fully express itself phenotypically in males, even though it is a recessive gene. Such genes are called sex-linked, and some inherited traits are sex-linked. Traits inherited through genes carried on nonsex chromosomes are inherited autosomally.

Even sex determination is not always as clear cut as xx=female, xy=male. It is known that the sex of alligators and certain turtles is not determined at the time the egg is fertilized. The sex of the hatchlings depends upon the mean incubation temperature of the eggs. In the American alligator, for example, temperatures of less than 30°C between the 7th and 21st days of incubation produce all females. Temperatures of more than 34°C produce all males.

In the case of turtles, temperature dependent sex determination has been demonstrated to occur with a number of species, but no general rule applies. Males from cool temperatures, females from warm, is the most common. In other species, however, a pattern of cool females, intermediate males, and warm females occurs. Finally, in others, sex determination is genetic.

In the case of sea turtles, knowledge of temperature dependent sex determination is of more than academic interest. When they come ashore and lay their eggs, most of the eggs are dug up and eaten by raccoons and other predators. The few that escaped this predation and returned to the ocean were sufficient to keep the populations stable. However, the activities of an ever-increasing human population, added to natural predation, have caused worldwide declines in sea turtle populations. One way to help populations recover is to prevent natural predation, and allow more hatchlings to return to the ocean. Biologists have dug up the eggs as soon as they are laid, and before raccoons find them, and incubated them artificially. In this way, all of the young can be put back into the ocean. However, unless the relationship between incubation temperature and sex determination of the species being saved is known, there is a real danger of defeating the purpose by producing turtles with a very lopsided sex ratio.

Females of a few species of animals can reproduce by a process called parthenogenesis. Their eggs can develop without being fertilized, and populations of these species consist entirely of females. This method of reproduction is common in some insects, but rare in vertebrates. Among reptiles, it is known in a number of lizard species and suspected in one snake, the braminy blind snake (*Typhlops braminus*), in which no males have been found. In America, several forms of whiptails (*Cnemidophorus*) are parthenogenetic. In parthenogenetic species, all heritable traits come from the female, and embryogenesis proceeds as with sexual reproduction. All-female populations are thought to be of hybrid origin. A possible survival advantage of all-female populations is that range expansion can occur without a pair entering a new territory. The major disadvantage is the failure of introducing new genes into the gene pool.

The understanding of genetics is made more difficult because the law of independent assortment of genes during meiosis may be modified. Genes assort independently during meiosis, but neighboring genes on the same chromosome often stick together during crossover. The term *linkage* is used for the tendency of genes located on the same chromosome to end up together in the same gamete. Sometimes genes with related functions are linked together, but in most cases genes are arranged haphazardly on chromosomes and linked genes may have independent functions.

Gene expression is not always tidy. The expression of almost all genes is influenced or modified to some extent by some other genes, and even by environment, and any one physical characteristic is likely to be controlled by more than one allelic pair.

PRACTICAL GENETICS: THE PUNNETT SQUARE

Many of the aberrant reptiles and amphibians discussed in this book represent proven gene mutations. In most cases, this was found out by F_1 crosses, or backcrossing an F_1 with a parent. Recall that F_1 refers to the first filial generation.

If two animals with known genotype are bred, the Punnett square, named for the British geneticist, G.C. Punnett, is a practical method of determining the most probable proportions of offspring of different genotypes and phenotypes. The square is made up by placing male and female gametes on different axes of a checkerboard. It is important to remember that in real test crosses, the offspring rarely occur in the exact predicted ratios.

A monohybrid cross involves a male and female, both heterozygous for the same trait. This can be illustrated by predicting the outcome of a cross between two animals heterozygous for the recessive trait, albinism.

Genes: A = wild-type gene
         a = albino gene

Phenotypes based on genotypes: AA = wild-type
                                Aa = wild-type
                                aa = albino

Cross: Aa × Aa

When the genes are assorted in meiosis, the gamete from either parent may contain either a dominant A gene or a recessive a gene. All possible gametes from each parent are lined up on the axes of a Punnett square.

	A	a
A	AA	Aa
a	Aa	aa

Results: 3 wild types (AA, Aa)
           1 albino (aa)

A dihybrid cross involves a male and female, both heterozygous for two characteristics. This can be illustrated by predicting the outcome of a cross between two blotched snakes each heterozygous for two recessive traits: albinism and striping.

Genes: A = wild type color   B = blotched
         a = albino   b = striped

Phenotypes based on genotypes: AABB = wild-type color with blotches
                                AABb = wild-type with blotches
                                AAbb = wild-type with striping
                                AaBB = wild-type with blotches
                                AaBb = wild-type with blotches
                                Aabb = wild-type with stripes
                                aaBB = albino with blotches
                                aaBb = albino with blotches
                                aabb = albino with stripes

Cross: AaBb × AaBb

All possible gametes from each parent are lined up on the axes of a Punnett square.

	AB	Ab	aB	ab
AB	AABB	AABb	AaBB	AaBb
Ab	AABb	AAbb	AaBb	Aabb
aB	AaBB	AaBb	aaBB	aaBb
ab	AaBb	Aabb	aaBb	aabb

Results: 9 wild-type color and blotches
           3 wild-type color with stripes
           3 albino with blotches
           1 albino with stripes

CONCLUSION

When I became interested in the genetics of abnormalities, it was common knowledge that a pairing of two albino snakes, or two albinos of anything for that matter, invariably resulted in all albino offspring. I was taught this in my first biology class in junior high school and my last biology classes in medical school. Many people still believe this, but we know now that it is not true.

Mendel's laws have not been repealed, but they are being amended and added to. DNA is still the basic gene, but technology and increases in information about the molecular basis of genes are expanding rapidly, augmenting our knowledge of the nature of DNA, the structure of the genes, the packaging of the genes in chromosomes, and importantly, the way organisms read and process the information contained in the DNA. As a result, new questions are arising faster than old ones are being solved, and this is true with reptiles and amphibians as with all other living forms.

4
Chromatophore Biology

Chromatophores are pigment cells, and abnormal colors in reptiles and amphibians are essentially developmental, structural, or functional chromatophore disorders. A knowledge of pigment cell biology is necessary if these anomalies are to be understood.

In all vertebrates, pigment cells arise from the embryonic neural crest as undifferentiated stem cells called chromatoblasts. The neural crest is part of the embryonic ectoderm that is also the precursor of the brain and spinal cord. Early in the course of embryogenesis, the chromatoblasts migrate to the skin (Fig. 4.1), where they differentiate into mature pigment cells. In cold-blooded vertebrates they differentiate into three fundamentally distinct chromatophore types: melanophores; xanthophores; and iridophores (Fig. 4.2). Even though all three types are derived from a common stem cell and have many features in common, they differ from one another in appearance, composition, and function. Also, because they arise in the neural crest, chromatophores have a physiological relationship to the nervous system not shared by the keratinocytes and cellular contents of the dermis. The chromatoblasts of warm-blooded vertebrates differentiate into only one chromatophore type, the epidermal melanocyte.

MELANOPHORES

Melanophores are dendritic cells that synthesize black and brown pigments known as melanin, a word derived from the Greek word for black. Dendrites are cytoplasmic projections of the main cell body. Within melanophores, the pigment is contained in intracellular organelles called melanosomes.

Melanophores are subdivided into dermal and epidermal melanophores, based on their location in the skin. Dermal melanophores are located in the upper dermis, and epidermal melanophores are scattered among the basal layer of keratinocytes in the lower epidermis. Though both types synthesize and contain melanin, they are clearly distinct from one another.

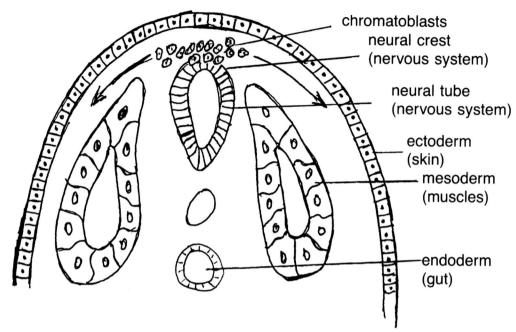

Fig. 4.1. Embryo scheme, transverse section.

Epidermal melanophores of cold-blooded vertebrates are anatomically and functionally the equivalent of epidermal melanocytes in warm-blooded animals, and any discussion of one may be applied to the other. Both function in morphological color change, such as seasonal changes and response to ultraviolet radiation. Because of this, they are required to synthesize melanin on a constant or recurrent basis, and they remain functionally active for the life of the organism.

The basic function of dermal melanophores is color pattern production, and rapid color change in those reptiles and amphibians that are capable of such changes. In vertebrates capable of these rapid changes in color, the dendrites are

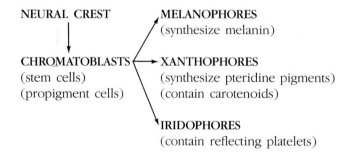

Fig. 4.2. Schematic interpretation of chromatophore formation.

prominent, since they play a key role in the process. Dermal melanophores, once adult coloration is established, have less need for further melanin synthesis, and are functionally more static.

The production of melanin (melanosynthesis) is essentially the conversion of a naturally occurring amino acid, tyrosine, to melanin. Amino acids are the structural units of protein molecules. In addition to being the precursor of melanin, tyrosine is also the precursor of thyroxine and adrenalin.

Melanin is an insoluble black or brown complex copolymer of tyrosine derivatives and proteins, and its synthesis involves a series of chemical reactions. The initial two steps, conversion of tyrosine to dopa (dihydroxyphenylalanine), and dopa to dopaquinone, are essentially oxidation reactions. These two chemical reactions cannot proceed in the absence of the catalyst tyrosinase. Tyrosinase (o-Diphenol oxidase) is a copper-protein complex synthesized by the melanophores. The actual synthesis takes place within the melanosomes, the intracellular organelles that bear the enzyme tyrosinase. In addition to being the site where melanin is synthesized, melanized melanosomes are the form in which melanin is transferred from the cell body into the dendrites. Dopaquinone then undergoes further metabolic elaboration to become melanin (Fig. 4.3).

XANTHOPHORES

The bright colored chromatophores of cold-blooded vertebrates are called xanthophores. They contain a variety of pigments including pteridines and carotenoids. The red and yellow pteridine pigments are synthesized by the xanthophores. Pteridine is a step in the biochemical pathway of the formation of folic acid from purines, and the enzyme xanthine dehydrogenase is known to participate in synthesis of at least some of the pteridine pigments. Pteridine pigments are usually the first pigments to appear in the xanthophores during ontogeny. They are contained in organelles called pterinosomes, analogous to the melanosomes in melanophores.

Carotenoids are a class of yellow to reddish pigments occurring in many vegetable oils and some animal fats. They are not synthesized by the xanthophores.

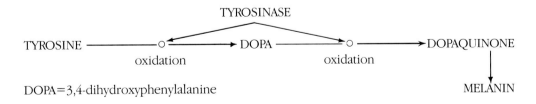

Fig. 4.3. Role of tyrosinase in early stages of melanosynthesis.

They are of dietary origin and are stored in xanthophores in vesicles of various sizes interspersed among the pterinosomes. Carotenoids generally make their appearance in xanthophores later in ontogeny.

The color of xanthophores depends on the combination of the pteridine pigments and carotenoids that they contain, and may be yellow, red, or intermediate shades of these two colors. Those that contain predominantly red pteridines (drosopterins) are called erythrophores on the basis of their appearance.

IRIDOPHORES

Iridophores do not synthesize pigments, but participate in color production by virtue of their physical properties. They contain crystalline deposits of purines, notably guanine, hypoxanthine, and adenine, in organelles called reflecting platelets. The platelets are usually arranged in oriented stacks. Reflection and scatter of incident light results in green, blue, red, and khaki hues. The form, size, and orientation of the reflecting platelets determine the reflected colors. Reflecting platelets vary in appearance between and within species.

5

Participation of Chromatophores in Color Pattern

CHROMATOPHORES IN SNAKES

Snakes' color patterns are their most obvious features. They are produced by the interaction of dermal chromatophores, epidermal melanophores, hemoglobins in the blood supply, and optical diffraction from the keratin layer of the epidermis. Of these, the principal participants are the dermal chromatophores. The role of the keratin layer is more important in iridescent species.

Common pattern types include bands, blotches, diamonds, rings, and stripes. They are genetically determined, are fairly consistent for each species, and in most cases serve for field identification. Some snakes have no pattern.

The smooth earth snake (*Virginia valeriae*) of south Georgia is a typical patternless species. Smooth earth snakes range from New Jersey and Pennsylvania south into Florida and west into Ohio and Mississippi. Because they are so nondescript, smooth earth snakes are often brought to me for identification, even by people who have a field guide. These tiny harmless snakes rarely exceed 18 cm (10 in). They are patternless light gray or brown, and very secretive. They are rarely seen crawling about, but are commonly unearthed by people working on their lawns, who nearly always assume that they have found a baby snake. Most people are surprised to learn that the small snake they found is an adult. Smooth earth snakes are easily confused with another locally common small brown snake, the rough earth snake (*Virginia striatula*). Both are a nondescript brown and about the same size, but the scales of the rough earth snake are keeled.

At the other extreme are snakes patterned with exquisite designs, incorporating many colors. A few, such as the Gaboon viper, possess an intricate pattern almost impossible to describe. Gaboon vipers are large heavy-bodied venomous African snakes averaging 91.5–122 cm (36–48 in), but sometimes reaching a length of 180 cm (6 ft). Though not the longest, they are one of the world's heaviest venomous snakes, and they are also known for their huge fangs and large venom yield. Their brown, beige, black, yellow, and purple colors are arranged in a bizarre pattern best described as resembling an oriental carpet. Even those who detest snakes might be inclined to call Gaboon vipers beautiful if they were not put off by the fact that they can be deadly.

With over 2000 species worldwide, many snakes share similar markings, and identification can be confusing. Other characters used by herpetologists to tell them apart include size, presence or absence of fangs, shape of pupils, presence of facial pits, body configuration, scale characteristics, and scale counts.

Except for epidermal melanophores, all snake chromatophores occupy a primary color zone in the upper dermis. Xanthophores and dermal melanophores are concentrated in a narrow zone immediately beneath the epidermis. Iridophores, where present, are immediately beneath the other two. The distribution, density, quantity, and quality of the contained pigments of these three cell types interact to determine the color and the pattern. This primary color zone contains the pigments responsible for the apparent color pattern in that area.

I examined full thickness skin biopsies from representative snakes to get a better idea of where the various chromatophores are located, and how they interact. The snakes were chosen first because they were readily available, but specifically to demonstrate various aspects of color production. A coral snake (*Micrurus f. fulvius*) was selected because of its three relatively pure colors (red, yellow, and black), sharply demarcated from one another. The scarlet kingsnake (*Lampropeltis triangulum elapsoides*) was selected to rule out species differences between it and the similarly colored coral snake. The southern copperhead (*Agkistrodon c. contortrix*) was selected as an example of a snake with heavily and lightly pigmented bands of the same general color: brown. A corn snake (*Elaphe g. guttata*) was selected because of its many colors of various hues.

Biopsies and other sections were prepared for examination by fixed tissue, frozen section, or both. For fixed tissue examination, biopsies were fixed in 10% formalin, paraffin blocks prepared after routine processing, and 5 micron sections were stained with hematoxylin and eosin (H&E). This general histologic stain provides some degree of differential staining of cytoplasmic and nuclear features as well as connective tissue components. Melanin is easily seen and frequently fills the cells to the exclusion of visible nuclei. In regard to the other chromatophores, red and yellow pigments are soluble and labile and easily decolorized by ordinary preserving and staining techniques, and their pigments may not be distinguished with H&E stains. Granules in iridophores are visible as slightly refractile pale brown to gold.

For frozen sections, samples from living or recently killed specimens were imbedded in OTC compound (optimum cutting temperature) and frozen with Cytocool (a tissue freezing aerosol) to minus 20°C. Six-micron sections were cut with an Ames cryostat, mounted as unstained sections with saline, and examined immediately. With this technique, xanthophores are visible in their natural colors.

Beneath the red band of the coral snake, a primary color zone in the upper dermis is occupied by a dense band of erythrophores, with occasional melanophores, either in the dermis or the epidermis, depending on the purity of the red color as it appeared on the snake's surface (Fig. 5.1). Beneath the yellow band, the

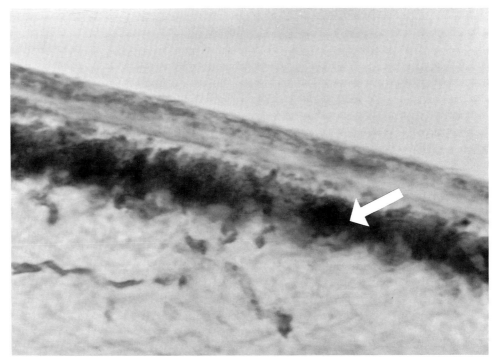

Fig. 5.1. Skin from red band of coral snake *Micrurus f. fulvius*, frozen section. Dense band of erythropores in upper dermis.

primary color zone is occupied by a thick layer of bright yellow xanthophores, numerous iridophores, and scattered epidermal melanophores (Fig. 5.2). The black band contains a thick layer of dermal melanophores, numerous epidermal melanophores, and no iridophores. When there is a sharp color demarcation across the surface of a scale, as when the cephalad half of the scale is black and the caudal half of the same scale is yellow, there are increased epidermal melanophores within the yellow part of the scale, compared with the number present in an adjacent scale that is completely yellow. This is visible on close examination of the snake. Histological findings of the scarlet kingsnake were identical.

In the copperhead, the primary color zone is occupied by yellowish xanthophores beneath the light bands and reddish xanthophores beneath the dark bands. Epidermal melanophores are present in all areas, but much more numerous in the areas of darker bands. Iridophores are abundant beneath the light bands, but also in surprising numbers beneath the darker bands.

Biopsies were performed on various areas of the corn snake. A black border of a dorsal blotch reveals a thick band of dermal melanophores, numerous epidermal melanophores with dendrites extending upward between the keratinocytes (Fig. 5.3), and no iridophores. The number of epidermal melanophores in red and yellow areas varies with the quality of these colors in individual snakes.

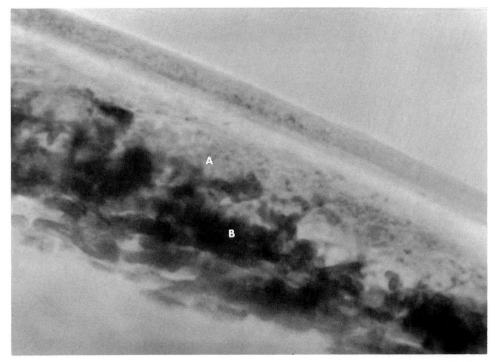

Fig. 5.2.   Skin from yellow band of coral snake *Micrurus f. fulvius*, frozen section. A, xanthophores; B, iridophores.

An albino corn snake was biopsied at two sites that would have been black in a normal snake, the border of a dorsal blotch and an abdominal rectangle. No chromatophores of any type were visible, but the cellularity in the tissue suggested that the pigment cells were present but not functional.

Pattern is largely determined by the melanophore-xanthophore complex situated in the upper dermis, while iridophores appear to play more of a role in determining the quality of the colors that make up the pattern. It is also possible that the iridophores, with their reflecting platelets, may play some role in protecting the organism from excessive ultraviolet radiation. Iridophores are most numerous beneath the areas of lightest coloration and essentially absent in black areas where melanin is present to absorb radiation.

Pigmentation in the epidermis is restricted to the presence of scattered melanophores in the basal layer (Figs. 5.4 and 5.5), and occasional deposits of melanin within the keratinocytes as migration to the surface occurs. Epidermal melanophores are apparently also important in color quality. In all of the biopsies the basal epidermal cells were in cuboidal arrangement, and the exposed surface of that part of the scale that contacts the ground had a thick keratinized squamous epithelium.

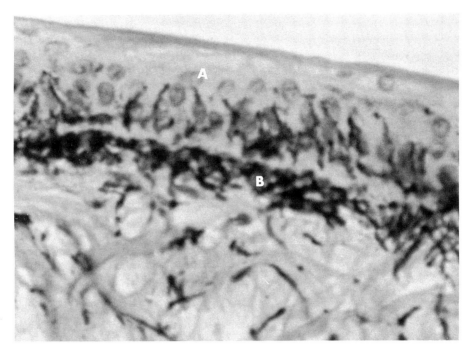

Fig. 5.3. Skin from black border of dorsal blotch of corn snake *Elaphe g. guttata*, H&E. A, epidermis; B, dermal melanophores.

CHROMATOPHORES AND PATTERN

The function of chromatophores and the way they interact to create color combinations is known to a large extent, and can be inferred from microscopic examination of skin biopsies, but the genesis of pattern formation is not completely understood. As the embryo develops, chromatoblasts leave the neural crest and spread ventrally across the skin, where they not only differentiate for different colors, but they also differentiate into chromatophore types in accordance with the pattern of the area that they are to occupy. The mechanics of pattern formation have prompted divergent opinions and more than one theory.

It is believed that, as the undifferentiated chromatoblasts enter the skin, they encounter a prepattern in the skin that induces them to locate and differentiate according to some microenvironment in the skin itself. The nature of this prepattern and the way in which chromatoblasts pick up clues from it can only be guessed.

An alternative theory that has been put forward is that pattern formation is an inherent function in the neural crest, and the differentiation of the chromatoblasts is determined at that point. In either event, pattern is determined genetically.

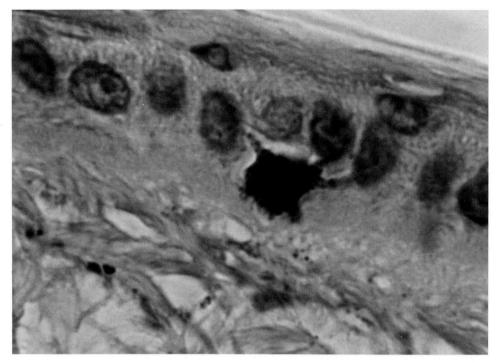

Fig. 5.4. Magnified epidermis. San Diego gopher snake (*Pituophis melanoleucus annectans*), showing epidermal melanophore.

Furthermore, evidence exists that the chromatoblasts, once differentiated into one of the three basic types, can transdifferentiate (redifferentiate) into one of the other types under certain circumstances. This is not surprising, since all three chromatophore types arise from a common stem cell, and share numerous characteristics.

Transdifferentiation could explain the remarkable ontogenetic changes in both color and pattern of the yellow rat snake (*Elaphe obsoleta quadrivittata*). Yellow rat snakes are large, handsome nonpoisonous snakes occurring on the United States coastal plain from North Carolina south through the Florida peninsula. They average 107–183 cm (42–72 in.), with a record of 213.4 cm (84 in). They prey on small mammals and birds, which are killed by constriction. Because they are distinctive and harmless, many people tolerate them, but they occasionally raid hen houses. Deserted farm buildings are good places to search for them, and it pays to look up, since they are excellent climbers. When first picked up, they release a strong musk which some people, Bette for example, consider unpleasant. They make hardy captives, and do not emit the musk after calming down.

Newly hatched specimens are strongly blotched, with dark brown blotches on a pale brown or gray background. As the snakes mature, the blotches fade and are replaced by four longitudinal black stripes, and the ground color changes to yellow. The brightest specimens with the most golden-yellow come from peninsular

Fig. 5.5. Magnified scale surface coral snake (*Micrurus f. fulvius*), with black-yellow junction crossing middle of scale. Arrow, epidermal melanophore.

Florida. Some cue, probably hormonal, prompts this remarkable ontogenetic change in both color and pattern.

CHROMATOPHORES AND COLOR CHANGE

Chromatophores, even though they are situated in the skin, have a developmental affiliation with the central nervous system, from which they originated. They respond to neural and hormonal influences and are responsible for changing color.

Reptiles and amphibians can change colors. Two types of color change take place: morphological and rapid.

Morphological color change is a slow process involving synthesis of melanin as a result of persistent stimulation. The changes are generally a response to seasonal changes in background conditions. These changes are not well-known in snakes. However, at least some rattlesnakes do have the power of color change, but the changes are not marked. These consist of lightening of some areas accompanying increases in temperatures. Physically, morphological color change is explained by increased melanosynthesis, dispersal of melanosomes within the melanophores, and accumulation of melanin in keratinocytes. Melanin accumulated in keratinocytes is visible as a vague pattern in the shed skin of most snakes.

At colder temperatures, basking lizards generally have dark skin to increase absorption from the sun's rays. When it becomes hotter, they lighten up to reflect radiation. Some lizards, as well as many frogs, are capable of astonishing color change.

The green anoles (*Anolis carolinensis*) that live outside our kitchen windows are typical of lizards with rapid color change. These pale green lizards with a pink throat fan are generally well-known to everyone in the southeastern United States from southern North Carolina south through Florida and west into Texas. In most places they are abundant, but they have been displaced in large areas of south Florida by the brown anole (*Anolis sagrei*), an aggressive lizard introduced from some Caribbean islands. Green anoles average 13–20.3 cm (5–8 in), most of their total length consisting of a long tail. They are climbers, found on buildings and plants. However, because of their remarkable ability to change color, they may not be pale green when first seen. At low temperatures they are generally brown, whether the lizard is in the shade or sunlight. They sleep green, and also turn green with excitement. They certainly do not change color to color-match their background, since brown anoles on green leaves and green anoles on dark siding are often seen. Because of these color changes, they are often called chameleons.

In those reptiles and amphibians capable of rapid color changes, the chromatophores are arranged in a functional unit designated as the "dermal chromatophore unit." Within the unit, the uppermost cells, hugging the underside of the epidermis, are xanthophores. Immediately beneath the xanthophores is a layer of iridophores. This may be a single or multiple layer, differing with species. The basal portion of the unit consists of melanophores, with prominent dendrites extending upward (Fig. 5.6).

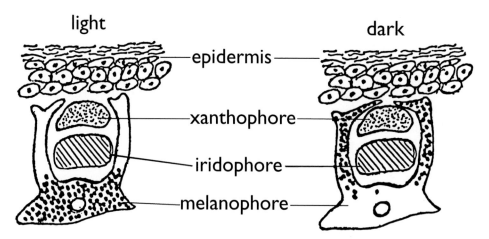

Fig. 5.6. Schematic representation: Dermal chromatophore unit showing melanin dispersal into dendrites during rapid color change

Rapid color change is made possible by the coordinated response of the three chromatophore types, and depends mainly on movement of melanin within the melanophores. When melanin is dispersed into the dendrites, it flows up, around, and over the other chromatophores, darkening the skin. The skin lightens when the melanin flows back into the cell body of the melanophores. At all times, the color is being determined by the interaction of all three melanophore types, and it is far more complicated than merely lightening and darkening. When the melanin flows back into the melanophore cell bodies in a brown-colored anole, the lizard does not merely lighten. It turns bright green as the xanthophores absorb various wavelengths being reflected from the iridophores. Anyone who has held one of these lizards in his hand has probably watched these remarkable changes take place.

True chameleons (family, Chameleonidae) are capable of such extraordinary color change that the word *chameleon* has even entered the English language to define a changeable or inconsistent person. Chameleons occur only in Africa, Asia, and extreme southern Europe. Their underlying principles of color changing are the same as anoles, but they are more sophisticated. They can change color and pattern, and they change for various reasons: for camouflage, to intimidate competitors, to initiate sex, or even to indicate that they are no longer interested in sex.

Ultraviolet radiation, temperature, light, emotions, and other external stimuli are capable of inducing color change. The actual movement of melanosomes into and out of the dendrites is mediated by MSH (melanocyte stimulating hormone), a secretion of the anterior pituitary gland, and intermedin, a hormone secreted by the intermediate lobe of the pituitary gland. Control mechanisms include the nervous system and hormones. Hormonal and nervous control are not the same for all species that have the ability for rapid color change.

6

Function of Coloration and Pattern

SNAKES

Coloration and pattern are for concealment in most cases. They provide passive protection from predators, and allow snakes to approach their prey without being detected. The specific manner in which a snake's pattern contributes to concealment is not immediately clear in many cases, and often can be surmised only when correlated with the natural history of the snake.

An example is the eastern diamondback rattlesnake (*Crotalus adamanteus*), a large, heavy-bodied venomous snake at home in the pinelands of the coastal plain from southern North Carolina through Florida and west into eastern Louisiana. Though adults average less than 180 cm (6 ft), the record is 240 cm (8 ft). They have a large head, and a large adult may well weight over 6 kg (15 lb). An adult of any size makes for an impressive encounter. They are typically light brown or yellowish, with dark brown or black diamond markings outlined by a row of yellowish scales. The head is striped conspicuously with black and white from the eyes to the angles of the jaw. The intricate and beautiful pattern seems almost designed to draw attention to the snake, and indeed one encountered crossing a sandy rural road cannot be missed. Most of them are not encountered in the open, however, and the same snake lying coiled in splashes of bright sunlight criss-crossed by shadows from brush and palmetto is easily stepped on. This is a good reason for wearing boots when tramping about in south Georgia.

Several years ago, on a winter day when the trees and bushes were almost bare of leaves, I accompanied Dr. Bruce Means, the herpetologist at Tall Timbers Research Station near Tallahassee, while he located radio-telemetered diamondbacks that he was studying. In two instances, even though we knew from the signal that we were within a few feet of a snake we were looking for, I could not see either one. Bruce had a good eye for spotting them and had to point them out before I could see them. Once pointed out, they came into sharp focus. One was lying almost at our feet at the base of some blackberry bushes, and the other was lying among pine needles beside a large log. Neither snake rattled, though both were nearly stepped on by four of us as we searched the area trying to spot them.

A number of juvenile eastern diamondbacks are eaten by hawks, mammals, and some snakes, but adults are at the top of the food chain and have essentially only one enemy: man. Due to urbanization and other activities, they are extinct or their numbers are greatly diminished over large portions of their original range. Where suitable habitat remains, they are killed on sight by nearly everyone, and systematically hunted for rattlesnake roundups and for their skins. They spend the mild southern winters in gopher tortoise burrows, where they are collected by "gassing" the burrow. This is illegal in several states, since the gasoline fumes not only drive the rattlesnakes from the burrows, but also kill some of the other animals that are sharing the burrows.

For many people, a snake is a snake, and they all look alike, but this is far from the case. They come in various sizes and an astounding variety of color patterns. They also differ in many ways aside from size, color, and pattern. Some are slender and some are heavy-bodied. Various species occupy different niches, are active at different times of the day, have specific preferred foods and individual methods of overcoming prey, and often have different predators to worry about.

Very few snakes are at the top of the food chain. To survive, they must obtain prey while at the same time avoiding being eaten by something else. Color pattern in all species has a common function: survival.

Cryptic patterns function in different ways. Some camouflage the snake by matching its color and outline to the background. Many arboreal snakes are uniform green. The usefulness of this color is obvious to anyone who has ever grabbed a vine, only to feel the vine trying to escape.

The patterns of some snakes cause predators to misdirect their attack and allow the snake to escape. Southern ringneck snakes (*Diadophis p. punctatus*) are an example. Their range extends from southern New Jersey south through peninsular Florida. They are small snakes, averaging 25–36 cm (10–14 in). A typical specimen is brown to black with a yellow neck ring. The underside is yellow with a row of black half moons, and the underside of Florida specimens is bright red posteriorly and beneath the tail. The purpose of this red is not evident until the snake is threatened. When attacked, the snake suddenly curls the tail, exposing the flash of scarlet, probably to draw attention to the tail and protect the more vulnerable head. These tiny snakes are nonpoisonous and completely inoffensive, do not bite, and would have trouble breaking the skin if they did. Their secretive habits and their color pattern are essentially their only protection.

A great number of snakes are striped or lined. When a striped snake is crawling in a discontinuous environment with only part of the snake in view, it creates the impression of a stationary target even while the snake is moving rapidly away. I experienced this illusion while hunting snakes in Arizona. The Sonora whipsnakes (*Masticophis bilineatus*), common in southern Arizona and Mexico, are long slender olive, gray, or brownish snakes with two or three light-colored stripes on the sides. They average 76.2–170.2 cm (30–67 in). They do not blend in with the arid open brush terrain that they inhabit, but rely on speed and the optical illusion of the striping to avoid capture. When I encountered my first one in the field, I stared transfixed at one spot. By the time I decided to make a grab for it, the snake had slithered out of sight.

Some snake species mimic others in color pattern, gaining some advantage from this. The most widely-known examples of mimicry are the venomous coral snake (*Micrurus fulvius*) and the harmless scarlet kingsnake (*Lampropeltis triangulum elapsoides*). Both are found in the southeastern United States with almost identical ranges, from North Carolina through Florida and west into eastern Louisiana. Both are encircled by a series of yellow, black, and red rings. Coral snakes average 51–76 cm (20–30 in), with a record of 120.7 cm (47½ in), while scarlet kingsnakes are slightly smaller, averaging 36–51 cm (14–20 in) with a record of 68.6 cm (27 in). The chief identification characters are the sequence of the rings. The scarlet kingsnake has a red snout and yellow rings separated from the red by black. The coral snake has a black snout, and the red rings abut the yellow rings. "Red next to yellow will kill a fellow. Red next to black is a friend of Jack," is the most common mnemonic used to help remember which is which. Coral snakes are very secretive, and frequently found in yards by people who do not suspect their presence. Although they have toxic venom and live near people, bites are rare, since most bites happen to people who are handling them. Both coral snakes and scarlet kingsnakes are searched for by tearing loose bark off dead stumps and overturning boards and tin. As soon as they are exposed, they make a mad dash for a hole in the ground or new cover. A snake collector has almost no time to decide whether or not to grab.

Another coral snake mimic in the southeastern United States is the harmless scarlet snake (*Cemophora coccinea*). Scarlet snakes are patterned dorsally with red saddles bordered by black, on a yellowish ground color, giving the appearance of rings when the snake is viewed from above. The colors do not encircle the body, however, and the belly is whitish.

Mimicry occurs in many reptiles and amphibians, but the purpose is not always clear. It has generally been regarded as two types: Batesian and Mullerian. In Batesian mimicry, a harmless edible species, the mimic, comes to look like a harmful or distasteful species (the model). In Mullerian mimicry, two or more harmful or distasteful species come to resemble each other.

Many watersnakes have a dark back and lighter colored underside. The dark topside blends with the substrate, and the underside is less visible to fish and other prey looking up from under the water.

Males and females of most snakes cannot be distinguished on basis of color or pattern. It would make life easier if they could be, because one of the most frequent questions that I get asked is, "How do you tell the males from the females?"

Banded rock rattlesnakes (*Crotalus lepidus klauberi*), are exceptional in that males and female differ in color. They frequent rocky arid and semiarid regions in parts of Arizona, New Mexico, Texas, and Mexico. They are small, averaging 40.6–82.9 cm (16–32⅝ in), and are typically patterned with widely spaced black or dark brown crossbars contrasting strongly against greenish or bluish-green in males, and gray to bluish-gray in females. In view of the fact that the vast majority of snakes use olfaction for sex identification, it is unlikely that color dimorphism serves this purpose. However, the function is not clear. Natural selection favors color matching that best camouflages a snake. Since both color morphs are good color matches for the lichen covered rocks that the snakes frequent, color matching hardly accounts for this dimorphism.

AMPHIBIANS: OTHER REPTILES

Amphibian color patterns serve the same function as color patterns in other vertebrates: survival. Dark dorsal surfaces and light undersides are common in amphibians, especially aquatic varieties, rendering them less visible from both above and below.

A number of frogs, such as the gray tree frog (*Hyla versicolor* and *Hyla chrysoscelis*) possess flash colors. These two species are identical in appearance, and can be told apart by their voices. They are small, averaging 3.2–5.1 cm (1¼–2 in), with a large range encompassing nearly all of the eastern United States from Minnesota, southern Canada, and Maine in the north to Texas and Florida in the south. They are warty, are capable of color change, and may be brown, greenish, or almost white. They are difficult to see when clinging to the bark of trees, and I found my first one by accidentally putting my hand on it while grabbing a tree for support on a hillside. The concealed surfaces of their inner thighs are bright orange or yellow mottled with black. These flash colors are invisible when the frog is at rest, suddenly exposed when the frog leaps, disappearing suddenly when the frog alights. Predators are easily confused or startled by this, giving the frog an extra moment to escape.

Many of the amphibians with toxic and distasteful secretions are also brightly colored. When a predator has caught and tried to eat one, it learns to avoid that particular species and everything that resembles it. So-called warning colors are known as aposematic coloration.

Though sexual dimorphic color patterns are not common in snakes or amphibians, they are more common among lizards. Broadhead skinks (*Eumeces laticeps*) are large rust-colored lizards, averaging 16.5–32.4 cm (6½–12¾ in). The range extends from southeastern Pennsylvania south into Florida and west into Kansas, Oklahoma, and Texas. The males' heads become bright red during the breeding season. They are called "red headed scorpions" by many southerners, who probably do not identify the more nondescript females as being of the same species. Unfortunately for the broadhead skinks, many poorly informed people think they are venomous and kill them. Immature ones have yellow stripes and a bright blue tail, are easily confused with other species of skinks in their range, and scale features must be examined to identify them.

The colors of many male lizards change in the breeding season. Fence lizards (*Sceloporus undulatus*) are small spiny arboreal lizards found throughout much of the southern half of United States from southern Pennsylvania south into Georgia and west into Kansas and Texas. They are common in open pine woods, and are often spotted on wooden fences and stumps, but are not always easy to catch. They escape by scurrying up any nearby tree, always moving higher and staying on the opposite side of the trunk. They average 10–18.4 cm (4–7¼ in). Females are generally gray with irregular lines across the back while males are usually brown with bright blue patches on the sides of the belly and at the base of the throat. These patches are exhibited when the male is defending his territory or in courtship. Most lizards are diurnal and rely on vision rather than chemical or tactile stimuli during courtship, and the function of color dimorphism is clear. The purpose of sexually dimorphic color patterns in many snakes and amphibians is not clear.

Lizards spend considerable time thermoregulating. When they come out in the morning, they need to get warmed up to get active. On cool mornings some lizards disperse melanin in the melanophores, darkening the skin and absorbing more radiant energy. They depend on the heat from the sun to propel growth, digestion, reproduction, and other body processes.

Herpetologists are aware that male and female box turtles have a fairly reliable difference in eye color. Males have red eyes, frequently bright red, while females' eyes are greenish or brownish.

—

7
Albinism

White pink-eyed squirrels climbing and scampering about in the lawns and parks are the pride of Olney, Illinois. Police display a picture of a white squirrel on their shoulder patches, and an ordinance grants squirrels the right-of-way on city streets. The entire population is said to have descended from a single albino pair discovered in a gray squirrel litter in 1902, and they have been pampered since then. Many homeowners encourage them with special feeding boxes, and animal lovers donate nuts and bread to feed those in the city parks. If it were not for white squirrels, very few people outside of Illinois would have ever heard of Olney.

In 1975 two lion cubs were born in the Timbavati Nature Reserve in South Africa. Many lion cubs were born in Africa that year without getting their picture in *Newsweek* magazine, and these two also would have gone unnoticed but for one thing. Both were white with brown noses and normal yellow eyes. In 1976 a third white cub was born to a different lioness in the pride. Zoologists had seen albino lions, but these were unlike any known albinos. It was speculated that the color anomaly was a mutation, and the three cubs were fathered by the same lion.

So many animals with abnormally decreased amounts of pigment have been grouped under the term *albino* that the term is hard to define. It may be defined as a congenital decrease or absence of melanin in the skin, mucosa, and eyes, and it is usually an inherited defect in melanin metabolism. Different types of albinism and different degrees of pigment loss account for differences in appearance of various albinos, and terms such as albinoid and albinistic have crept into the language. The word is derived from *albus*, the Latin word for white, and albino is primarily reserved to describe those with complete or nearly complete lack of melanin.

Albinism is widely distributed throughout the animal kingdom, occurring in insects, fish, reptiles, amphibians, birds, and mammals. Though uncommon, it has been recorded in nearly every animal of which an adequate number have been observed, and is thought to be a universal recurring mutation. The incidence has been roughly estimated at 1:10,000 to 1:40,000 individuals, but this is a rough guess since the incidence cannot be estimated in rare animals of which only a limited number of individuals have been observed.

A form of albinism even occurs in plants. White replaces green in albino plants because the mutation prevents the synthesis of chlorophyll. In plants, the mutation is lethal, since without chlorophyll, they cannot trap the energy of sunlight to convert water and carbon dioxide into carbohydrates. As soon as the seedlings use up the energy stored in the seed, they wither and die.

The word *albino* was first used about 1660 by a Portuguese explorer to describe white Africans that he had seen in his voyages. Though it is universal to all races, albinism is more striking in individuals surrounded by a population of normally dark skinned people, which may be why it so profoundly impressed early explorers to Africa.

Different cultures have regarded albinos in different ways, from demigod to outcast. Historically, many may have been confused with lepers, since leprosy frequently causes various degrees of depigmentation, and lepers were the lowest of outcasts in some societies. The first Europeans to explore the Americas encountered some populations with high incidence. They did not know that albinism is a mutation that arose spontaneously in those populations, and speculated that some white Europeans had preceded them to America and multiplied.

The incidence of albinism is much higher than average in the Cuna Indians, the descendants of a highly developed civilization that occupied Central America. This civilization was destroyed by contact with Europeans during the Spanish conquest, and present-day remnants occupy the San Blas Islands and nearby coast of Panama. A pure race with considerable inbreeding, they are known to science for their high albino incidence of about 1:100. This compares with an estimated incidence of about one albino in 20,000 for the human race in general. Albino Cuna Indians are called "moon children" because their eyes cannot tolerate bright sunlight, and they usually go outdoors only after the sun goes down. In addition, nystagmus and other visual anomalies are common among them. Ordinary sunlight also ages their skin prematurely. In some animals, and this possibly includes man, an abnormality of the nerve tracts from the eye to the brain may be associated with the albino mutation.

Recessive mutations do not ordinarily become common in a population, particularly in animal or bird populations. The usual course of events is for the recessive albino gene to persist or recur in the gene pool of any population, with an albino phenotype cropping up sporadically. In most animals, nature selects against the survival of albinos. They are conspicuous, and those low on the food chain are more susceptible to predation. Larger predatory species may be less successful in approaching prey without being detected. All albino animals that rely on vision are handicapped by photosensitivity, and possibly other eye defects. Any harmful effects from ultraviolet radiation are magnified. It is even possible that albinos may have trouble finding a mate in some visually oriented species. The incidence can increase only through selection in favor of albinism or against the normal. Though nature rarely if ever selects for albinism, artificial selection is commonly used to produce pure lines of albinos, particularly white laboratory mice and rats. Inbreeding in a population, for any reason, increases the incidence.

Because it is conspicuous as well as being widespread, albinism has intrigued people from the time it was first noted. Early observers suspected that the disorder was inherited when they noted that it is more common where other albinos are found. It was not until 1902, however, that its inheritance in mice was demonstrated as a Mendelian recessive. Subsequently, as albinos of other animals have been collected and bred, the same mode of inheritance has been found in nearly all of them. From time to time matings have produced unanticipated results, and it is now known that not all animals with diminished pigmentation have the same genetic defect.

MELANIN METABOLISM

Albinism was one of the first inborn errors of metabolism to be intensively investigated, probably because it affects man. It quickly became evident that the study of albinism and the study of melanin metabolism are inseparable, and by 1913 the general outlines of melanin production and its relationship to albinism were understood.

Most investigations of melanin metabolism have been performed with mice, other laboratory mammals, and some with amphibians, but very little with snakes. In general, all of the important discoveries leading to our understanding of melanosynthesis and albinism have some application to the study of albinism in snakes, since the composition and synthesis of melanin are common to all vertebrates.

TYPES OF ALBINISM

Albinism may be classified in one of several ways: areas of involvement; degree of involvement; and genetic defect. All forms are inherited congenital conditions with absent or diminished melanin formation, but separate mutations at various loci affecting pigmentation each can cause albinism. Not every type has been seen in every vertebrate species. In particular, not every known type has been described in reptiles and amphibians.

Areas of Involvement

Albinism may be classified to indicate which parts of the system are affected. Oculocutaneous albinos contain no melanin in eyes or skin. Ocular albinism is a rare mutation known in man. Affected persons have ocular findings the same as those in oculocutaneous albinism, but normal skin pigmentation. Ocular albinism is caused by a sex-linked recessive mutation. When pigment loss involves only portions of the skin, it usually goes under other names, such as vitiligo or piebald.

Degree of Involvement

Just as "not every animal with decreased pigment is an albino," not every albino is completely devoid of melanin. The classical mutated recessive genes at the albino locus, in the homozygous state, results in complete lack of melanin. Alternative recessive mutations at the same locus allow for a degree of melanosynthesis in the homozygous state. Some hypomelanistic reptiles and amphibians are actually true albinos even though they contain some melanin.

Genetic Defect

Melanosynthesis requires a functional melanophore (melanocyte in mammals), but many steps are involved between the fertilization of the egg and the mature embryo. The chromatoblasts must differentiate from the other cells in the neural tube and successfully migrate to the skin; the skin environment must be appropriate for differentiation of the chromatoblasts into chromatophores; the melanophores must be able to synthesize tyrosinase; and melanosomes must form. A large number of genes at different loci control every step in this process. In mice, over 130 genes at 50 loci are known to influence coloration. It is likely that future research will prove that reptiles and amphibians have a similar number. Some hypomelanistic reptiles and amphibians that are not true albinos may represent mutations at sites other than the albino locus.

Tyrosinase-negative albinism is the most widely known form. The melanophore, to be able to synthesize melanin, must first be able to synthesize tyrosinase, and this synthesis is controlled by a pair of genes. A mutated recessive gene at this albino locus causes albinism by preventing synthesis of tyrosinase if both genes of the pair are recessive.

If all albinism was the result of an identical mutation, the mating of any two albinos should invariably produce albinos. However, not all albinism is tyrosinase-negative. Normal offspring from the mating of two albinos indicates the presence of other albino mutations. The albinism in each parent results from a different mutation, and each mutation causes albinism through a different mechanism.

The second most common albino mutation is designated tyrosinase-positive, because organisms homozygous for this mutation can synthesize tyrosinase. Yet, even though their pigment cells contain both tyrosine and tyrosinase, the essential ingredients for melanosynthesis, this type of albino cannot manufacture melanin. It will be recalled from chapter 4 that the actual synthesis of melanin takes place within the melanosomes. In tyrosinase-positive albinism, the tyrosinase cannot react with tyrosine, because the tyrosine is not transmitted into the melanosomes. The presence of tyrosinase inhibitors could also prevent melanosynthesis in tyrosinase-positive albinism.

Though tyrosinase-negative and tyrosinase-positive albinos have separate genotypes, the phenotypes are identical or nearly so. However, since tyrosinase-positive albinos synthesize tyrosinase, there exists the possibility of melanosynthesis taking place if at any time some of the enzyme gains access to some tyrosine. Because of this leakage, some tyrosinase-positive albinos may develop some pigmentation in the eyes as they age. Tyrosinase-negative albinos, at least in theory, should not be able to synthesize melanin under any circumstance.

DOPA REACTION

The dopa reaction is a histochemical test to demonstrate the presence of tyrosinase. It is based on the fact that the first two chemical reactions in melanosynthesis, the transformation of tyrosine to dopa and the transformation of dopa to dopaquinone, cannot take place in the absence of tyrosinase (see Fig. 4.3).

Briefly, a fresh biopsy of albino skin is incubated for a prescribed time in a solution of dopa. If tyrosinase is present in the biopsy specimens, the melanophores become visible because of the deposition of granular intracytoplasmic melanin. If tyrosinase is not present, the clear melanophores remain clear after incubation in the dopa. The test can be used to determine whether a particular albino specimen is tyrosinase-negative or tyrosinase-positive.

In regards to snakes, dermal melanophores are basically concerned with color pattern formation. After the adult coloration and pattern have been established, they contain little tyrosinase because they no longer have need for it. Even in tyrosinase-positive albino snakes, dermal melanophores deposit very little melanin in the dopa reaction.

Epidermal melanophores (melanocytes), on the other hand, are concerned with darkening for seasonal changes and protection from ultraviolet radiation, and the skin darkens and lightens repeatedly for the life of the snake. As the skin darkens, melanin is transferred to keratinocytes, and is lost with the next cast. This physiological activity calls for the cells to synthesize substantial amounts of tyrosinase. As a result the epidermal melanophores in tyrosinase-positive albino snakes are very sensitive to the dopa reaction.

8
Albinism and Hypomelanism
in Reptiles and Amphibians

SNAKES

An abnormally high number of albino Japanese rat snakes (*Elaphe climacophora*) has existed for many years in the city of Iwakuni, Japan.[1] Japanese rat snakes are typically light olive with four light brown longitudinal stripes. As with many snakes of this genus, the young are blotched. Adult albinos are white to yellow with golden irises, red pupils, and red tongues. Juvenile albinos are marked by orange dorsal and lateral blotches corresponding to the juvenile pattern. Since this is the only known instance among snakes where albinism has become established in a wild population, the habitat known to support the albino population was designated a natural monument in 1924 by the Japanese government, and in 1972 the snakes themselves were designated as the natural monument.

Their numbers are apparently decreasing, and not much is known about their historical abundance. Censuses since 1974 have shown progressive declines in reports of albinos, but wild types are still abundant. Because of this, the city and the Society for the Conservation of the Iwakuni shirohebis sponsored a study to elucidate the circumstances surrounding the establishment and maintenance of this unusual population. In 1924 residents of Iwakuni were questioned regarding these snakes. Snakes were reported to be abundant in stone walls, gardens, and streets, and it was not rare to find albino snakes in human residences. An artificial breeding program has been established to make sure that Iwakuni does not lose its unusual distinction among Japanese cities.

The shirohebis are true albinos, but many snakes with diminished pigmentation are not. True albinism in snakes is a congenital decrease or absence of melanin in the skin, mucosa, and eyes. It is usually an inherited metabolic defect in melanin metabolism, but developmental and structural defects can also result in diminished skin melanin, as discussed in Chapter 7. In addition, nutritional deficiencies including insufficient copper, which is an essential ingredient of tyrosinase, could also interfere with normal pigmentation.

Not all snakes with diminished melanin fit our preconceived notion of what an albino snake should look like, leading to a confusion of terms. A number of years ago the United States Supreme Court was considering laws against pornography, and none of the justices could define it. Finally, Justice Potter Stewart said, "I can't define it, but I know it when I see it." I feel the same way about albinism in snakes. I know the classical form, the form with no melanin (amelanistic), when I see it. For most herpetologists, the term *albino* is reserved for reptiles and amphibians that look like an albino should. Unfortunately, not all of them do look like they should.

A huge pool of anomalous reptiles and amphibians with diminished melanin are lumped under the term hypomelanistic. Hypo is defined as less than normal or deficient. They have a degree of melanin, and range from the almost classical albino to those with a nearly normal melanin complement. Hypomelanistic phenotypes are unpredictable, and are often described on the basis of their appearance: yellow albinos, xanthic albinos, and red albinos, for example. Hypomelanism is an imprecise term at best, and some of the reptiles and amphibians lumped in this group possibly have multiple chromatophore defects. For those, suffice to say they are hypopigmented.

Albinism in the Gopher Snake

The mode of inheritance of albinism in a snake was first demonstrated in the San Diego gopher snake (*Pituophis melanoleucus annectens*), a common snake in coastal southern California and part of Baja California. San Diego gopher snakes are fairly heavy-bodied snakes, averaging 105–150 cm (3.5–5 ft). They are typically patterned with black dorsal blotches that are irregularly connected with each other and the adjacent lateral series anteriorly, against a background color suffused with gray. When threatened, they hiss, inflate their bodies, and vibrate their tails. Because of this alarming behavior, along with their size, they are often mistaken for rattlesnakes and killed. This is sad, since they are harmless and the huffing and puffing is bluster. They often strike without even opening their mouths. They feed on rodents, which are killed by constriction, and they should be protected. Albino specimens turn up fairly frequently. In albinos, the black dorsal blotches are replaced by pink, and the background is yellowish.

C. B. "Si" Perkins, a long-time and well-known curator of the San Diego Zoo, was a pioneer in captive snake husbandry, and the zoo has always been known for its excellent reptile collection. He demonstrated the genetics of albinism starting with a female albino gopher snake collected in 1940.[2] She was bred first to a wild type (normal color and pattern), and laid three eggs. The two that hatched produced wild types. In 1945 a wild-type F_1 male from the first mating was back-crossed to the albino mother, resulting in four eggs. One was infertile, and the other three hatched albinos. Finally, in 1947, Perkins satisfied himself regarding the heredity by back-crossing the original female with an F_2 albino. Five eggs were laid, and all five were albinos. This was consistent with an autosomal recessive mutation.

Albinism in the Corn Snake

We were able to demonstrate an autosomal recessive mode of inheritance for albinism in the corn snake in 1959.[3] Corn snakes are medium-sized nonpoisonous snakes found in the southeastern United States from southern New Jersey south through Florida and west into Louisiana. Adults average 76–122 cm (30–48 in). They are typically patterned dorsally with longitudinally arranged black-bordered red or brownish-orange blotches against a background color that ranges from orange to gray. Small similar blotches alternate with the dorsal blotches, and a third series, alternating with the lateral series, involves the ends of the ventrals and the adjacent two or three scale rows. The underside is white conspicuously marked with black squares and rectangles. The quantity and quality of red, orange, and yellow pigments vary considerably in individual snakes. These snakes are thought to be called corn snakes because their belly markings resemble the checkered patterns of the kernels on Indian corn. At any rate, they are handsome snakes by any criteria.

They spend much of their time underground prowling through rodent burrows, and may be quite abundant even in residential areas without being noticed. They feed on small rodents, which are killed by constriction.

In addition to being handsome, corn snakes adapt well to captivity. They become docile, and generally feed well if offered mice, their favorite food.

Our colony was established in 1952 when I purchased an adult female specimen from Ross Allen, the founder of the Silver Springs Reptile Institute in Ocala, Florida. Ross discovered the spring before it was surrounded by urban development, and made it a tourist attraction with his reptile display. The collection contained a large number of native reptiles including huge alligators and many eastern diamondback rattlesnakes. Silver Springs was a magnet for every amateur herpetologist including me, and Ross was also one of the few sources for exotic snakes. Prior to World War II an exotic snake was any snake other than those occurring near home. The only other source was the local fruit wholesaler, where an occasional boa (*Boa constrictor*) stowed away in a banana shipment from Central America.

The corn snake was gravid when we received her, and by 1959 we had developed a colony of three generations. That year we obtained a male albino corn snake on breeding loan through the kindness of Max Hensley, a herpetologist at Michigan State University. Max had solicited museums, zoos, and private collections to determine the occurrence and relative frequency of albinism in North American reptiles and amphibians. Among his responses he located a live male albino corn snake.[4] It had been collected in 1953 in Stanly County, North Carolina, near Albemarle, and was maintained alive at the Charlotte Children's Museum.

The snake was mated with three wild types in 1959, resulting in 46 eggs, which all hatched. All of the hatchlings were pigmented normally, and ten were retained for future breeding. By 1961 the F_1's, though still small, were sexually mature, and a male F_1 was crossbred with three sibling F_1's. The three deposited a total of 31 eggs, some of them small and infertile. The first clutch began hatching the morning of August 31. Six normally colored snakes had poked their heads out of the eggs when I left for the office that morning. Bette asked, "Are you sure we will get albinos?" I reassured her. Later in the morning my secretary interrupted my work to tell me that my wife was on the phone with an important message. A small pink snout was protruding from one of the eggs. Of the 24 eggs from the three clutches that either hatched or contained identifiable embryos, seven were albino and 17 were wild types, slightly more than the one out of four predicted for a Mendelian recessive.

Albino corn snakes differ from wild types only in their lack of melanin. They are patterned normally with pink or red blotches against a yellowish or whitish background, but individual variation in the quantity and quality of these colors is considerable. An occasional specimen is actually patterned in two shades of red. The black borders of the blotches are replaced by white, and the venter lacks the bold black rectangles. Newly hatched specimens have little or no yellow in the background color, but the colors become rich as the snakes mature.

These findings were reconfirmed by Groves[5] in 1965, using F_1 snakes (heterozygous for albinism) that we had given him in 1959. After 1959, albino corn snakes were acquired by others who in turn bred them to produce pure albino strains. The photograph (Fig. 8.1) of our first clutch of eggs to contain albinos depicts, in one picture, all of the known captive albino corn snakes at that time. By 1993 this one-time curiosity has become common, and it is believed that nearly all of the thousands in existence today are descended from the lone albino snake collected in North Carolina in 1953.

Fig. 8.1.   First corn snake (*Elaphe g. guttata*) clutch containing albinos, 1961.

Incidence

Reports of individual occurrences of albinism in snakes are common in herpetological literature, newspapers, and magazines. In his survey of albinism in North American reptiles and amphibians, Hensley[4] recorded more than 100 albino or albinistic snakes in 16 genera. This survey in 1957 stimulated my interest in this subject. By now, so many albinos of various species of reptiles and amphibians have been collected that they are no longer routinely reported in major herpetological journals, and there is a growing understanding that for every species "to not find one sooner or later" may be more news than finding one. Furthermore, the explosive growth of snake husbandry, resulting in the production of thousands of individual snakes, has been uncovering albinism in many species that had no previous reports.

When Jeanette Covacevich, senior curator of vertebrates at the Queensland Museum in South Brisbane, Australia, visited the United States in 1993, she was amazed at the number of albino snakes and commented that albinism did not seem to be as widely reported in Australia. She furnished me with my slide of an albino yellow-faced whipsnake (*Demansia psammophis*), an elapid snake with a range including nearly all of Australia except parts of the Northern Territory and nearby Queensland and Western Australia. The family of snakes, Elapidae, includes cobras, the coral snake of America, and many Australian snakes. All have immovable front fangs and are venomous. Yellow-faced whipsnakes average 90 cm (228.6 in), and are rarely large enough to be dangerous. They vary in color, tending to uniform steely-gray above in southeastern populations, and gray above with dorsal reddish zone in northeastern populations. A distinctive dark streak edged with yellow extends from the eye to the angle of the mouth. Of the 3600 preserved snakes in the Queensland Museum, this snake and one other albino of another species were the only albinos in the entire collection.

The exact incidence of albinism in snakes is not known, but extrapolating from what is known about albinism in other vertebrates, it is likely to be in the order of 1:10,000 to 1:30,000 in the general population, though it is not necessarily the same for all species. Every now and then someone asks me the chance of finding a heterozygous carrier. This question usually comes from someone who has been fortunate enough to find an albino snake in the wild. If the incidence is 1:10,000, about one of every 50 wild types in the general population would carry the gene. With an incidence of 1:30,000, slightly over one of every 100 wild types would be a carrier. It is somewhat astonishing that so many individual snakes in a population carry a recessive gene of a condition that is rare in a general population.

The incidence of heterozygous carriers would not be uniform throughout the general population. It would be higher in the populations immediately surrounding the site where an albino was collected. No test is available to determine if a wild-type snake is heterozygous for the albino gene.

Young herpetologists should not be misled by the fact that albino snakes of many species can be purchased at the local pet store for a nominal price. In the wild they are rare, and the average collector is unlikely ever to experience the thrill of picking up a piece of corrugated metal and finding an albino snake.

Nonallelic Albinism in Snakes

The existence of nonallelic albinism in snakes was brought home to me in the course of breeding black rat snakes (*Elaphe o. obsoleta*)[6], at a time when I was only vaguely aware that more than one type of albinism was known. We had in our collection a male albino specimen that was collected in Virginia in 1957, and was given to us by Lear Grimmer, a herpetologist at the National Zoo. We obtained on a breeding loan a female albino specimen through the kindness of David Jardine, curator of herpetology at the Cincinnati Zoo. This snake was hatched in 1969 from eggs laid by a wild type collected in the Cincinnati region. The snakes were bred in 1976, resulting in 15 eggs. To our astonishment, the 14 that hatched were all wild types.

Tommy Logan, curator of herpetology at the Houston Zoo, described a similar incident involving albino western diamondback rattlesnakes (*Crotalus atrox*) (personal communication, 1976). Western diamondback rattlesnakes are big heavy-bodied poisonous snakes occupying a range extending from western Arkansas to southeastern California and from Oklahoma south into Mexico. Much of this range contains arid and semiarid grasslands, brushy terrain, and rocky canyons, all good places to find a specimen. Though they average 76–183 cm (30–72 in), the record is 213 cm (83⅞ in). They are generally brown or gray, often with dusty appearance, and possess indistinct diamonds. They are often called "coontail" rattlers because the tail pattern differs from the rest of the body by broad black and white rings. In sheer size, they are among the world's largest venomous snakes. They are dangerous, and account for more serious snakebites than any other species in America. Albinos are generally yellowish with tan diamond markings, with the tail ringed in white and tan.

In 1970 a female albino from the Houston Zoo was mated to a male albino from the Dallas Zoo. The female had been born to a wild type that was gravid when captured in 1959 in the valley region of Texas. The male was wild-caught as a youngster at Walnut Springs, TX. This mating resulted in 24 young. Even though the circumstances of the mating all but precluded the possibility of delayed fertilization from a prior mating, all 24 were normally pigmented.

Finally, in 1978, John Ruiz, a herpetologist from California, mated two albino San Diegan gopher snakes and all of the hatchlings were normally pigmented (personal communication, 1978). At the time, I had access to a laboratory with the reagents needed to subject tissue to the dopa reaction, and John was kind enough to make the original pair available to me. Tests demonstrated that the albino male was tyrosinase-negative and the female tyrosinase-positive.[7]

I subsequently had an opportunity to subject biopsies of the black rat snakes to the dopa reaction. Those from the gene pool from the snake collected in Virginia were tyrosinase-negative and those from the Cincinnati gene pool were tyrosinase-positive.

Multiple Alleles for Albinism

In 1967, before I realized that true albinos could be albinos and still contain a degree of melanin, we acquired a hypopigmented male black rat snake that was captured in 1974 in Pulaski County, Arkansas. He was generally yellowish in color (xanthic), with no discernible pattern, and had brown eyes. He was bred with a normally pigmented specimen, producing all normal offspring. Crossbreeding of F_1's demonstrated that the decreased pigment in this snake was caused by an autosomal recessive mutation. A pure strain was produced for further breeding experiments.[6]

When the original male was bred with a tyrosinase-positive albino, all of the young were hypomelanistic, phenotypically intermediate in pigmentation between the xanthic specimen and a completely amelanistic specimen. The results indicate the presence of three alternative alleles at the tyrosinase-positive albino locus. The two recessive albino alleles are each recessive to the wild type, but neither recessive gene is dominant to the other.

Skin biopsies from a xanthic (hypopigmented) albino and a completely amelanistic tyrosinase-positive albino were subjected to the dopa reaction (discussed in Chapter 7). Before the test, no pigment was visible in the melanophores of either biopsy. After incubation in dopa, melanin was deposited in the melanophores of both biopsies, but there was much more in the xanthic specimen and even some in the dermal melanophores. The xanthic mutation is a form of tyrosinase-positive albinism, allelic with the amelanistic tyrosinase-positive mutation. However, in spite of the metabolic defect, snakes with the xanthic mutation possess the capacity to synthesize small amounts of melanin even when homozygous for the mutation.

The Albino Phenotype Explained

We have always had live snakes in our home, and have had albino snakes of one variety or another since 1959. When we have visitors, nearly all of them want to see the snakes, often protesting how much they hate snakes even while they are looking at them. Even people who hate snakes are intrigued by the albinos. The most frequent question I get is, "Why aren't they white?" This question is not illogical, since most albino animals and birds are white, and most albino snakes aren't. Albino snakes of nearly every species are pigmented to some degree, and most of them possess a pattern composed of some shade of red, yellow, tan, or a combination of these colors.

In many species, the albino phenotype is more colorful than the wild type, and the albino black rat snake is a good example. Black rat snakes are large non-poisonous snakes found from southern Vermont south into Georgia and west into Oklahoma, Kansas, and southern Minnesota. They average 107–183 cm (42–72 in), with an unlikely but authentic record of 256.5 cm (101 in). They are strong constrictors, feeding on small mammals and birds. Like other rat snakes, they are good climbers. Abandoned farms and sawmills are excellent places to search for them. Black rat snakes were the first large snakes that I became familiar with, and I never tired of rooting through sawdust and wooden slabs around abandoned sawmills, searching for them in the mountains near Johnstown. They frequently laid their eggs in the sawdust piles. In Pennsylvania, they are called pilot blacksnakes because of a belief that they warn rattlesnakes and copperheads of danger and lead them to safety. This is not true, but it is true that any good place to hunt rattlesnakes is also a great place to hunt black rat snakes.

Adult black rat snakes are shiny black, with white, yellow, orange, or red skin between the scales. Immature specimens are gray with dark blotches, and adults sometimes show traces of the juvenile pattern, especially in portions of the range where intergradation occurs with related subspecies or after the skin is distended by a large meal.

For some reason, black rat snakes have more than their share of albinos, and I have seen a number of specimens from various parts of the range. Most are yellowish with prominent pink or even red blotches corresponding with the juvenile pattern.

The explanation for this albino phenotype was not fully understood even by herpetologists until fairly recently. I saw my first albino black rat snake in 1955 at the National Zoo. It was labeled "ALBINO CORN SNAKE," since it was assumed even then that an albino black rat snake would be white with pink eyes.

The difference in appearance between albino warm-blooded animals and albino cold-blooded animals stems from fundamental differences in their pigmentary system. Recall that mammals and birds possess only one pigment cell type: the epidermal melanocyte, and they have only one pigment in their skin: melanin. Yet, even though they can synthesize only this one pigment, most birds and many mammals possess patterns composed of many colors. Epidermal melanocytes synthesize black and brown pigments called eumelanin. When sulfur in the form of cysteine is incorporated into the tyrosine-melanin pathway, epidermal melanocytes synthesize red and yellow melanins called phaeomelanin. Aside from the fact that eumelanins and phaeomelanins are different in color, they are produced in the same biochemical pathway, and tyrosinase is the essential enzyme in either case. The albino mutation in warm-blooded vertebrates prevents melanosynthesis without regard to the color of the melanin.

In snakes, melanophores produce black and brown melanin, while the red and yellow pigments are synthesized by xanthophores. Since the albino mutation is specific for melanosynthesis, the xanthophores and iridophores are unaffected. They function normally, creating colorful patterns in most cases. In effect, in an albino snake, the black pigment is conveniently stripped away, allowing one to observe what the other chromatophores are doing. The reds and yellows in albino reptiles and amphibians are generally more pure and intense than the same colors in the wild types of the same species, since they are not obscured by the small amount of melanin that is present in the epidermal melanophores and keratinocytes of most wild types.

In hypomelanistic snakes, varying amounts of melanin are present. In the lighter ones, with less melanin present and more nearly approximating complete albinism, the other chromatophores contribute more to the color mix. In darker ones, with more melanin, the contribution of the other chromatophores is more obscure. For this reason, it is difficult to predict and even interpret the hypomelanistic phenotypes.

ALBINISM IN OTHER REPTILES AND AMPHIBIANS

Albinism in all organisms has the same principles. No specific surveys for records of lizards, turtles, crododilians, or amphibians have been published, but individual occurrences are published from time to time in scientific journals. From the slides that I have viewed, as well as from individual specimens that I have seen, albino phenotypes in this group of reptiles and amphibians are consistent with what would be expected when black is removed from the pigment mix.

The most widely known albinism in amphibians is the neotenic Mexican axolotl (*Ambystoma mexicanum*), since axolotls are raised in laboratories by the thousands and used for experimental purposes. Adult salamanders of most members of this genus are terrestrial, typically hatching as legless aquatic larvae and metamorphosing into limbed terrestrial adults. The axolotls of the Mexican plateau typically spend their entire life in water, becoming sexually reproductive adults while retaining larval characteristics, such as gills. The external gills of axolotls are very prominent. This retention of juvenile traits by a sexually mature salamander is called paedomorphosis, and can arise from slow development of the body relative to the gonads (neoteny) or from precocious gonadal development (progenesis). Though best known in axolotls, many other salamanders are paedomorphic. For periods of drought, however, axolotls have retained the ability to metamorphose into land-dwelling salamanders.

Axolotls are typically an olive green. Both larval and adult albino axolotls are yellow. Microscopic examination of albino axolotl skin reveals normal xanthophores and iridophores, with melanophores unpigmented but present.[8]

The albino gene was introduced into the axolotl gene pool by hybridization with an albino tiger salamander. Tiger salamanders are large, averaging 18–21 cm (7–8¼ in), with a record length of 33 cm (13 in). They are found in suitable habitats in most of the eastern half of the United States from Minnesota and Long Island south, though they are missing in most of the Appalachian uplands, the lower Mississippi delta region, and the southern half of the Florida peninsula. Suitable habitat may be any woodland with ample logs and debris to burrow under, and near breeding ponds where they congregate in the early spring. Except at breeding time, most are collected by picking up cover. They are dull black to deep brown with irregular yellowish spots on the dorsal and lateral surfaces. Both albino tiger salamanders that I have seen were yellow with violaceous perpendicular lateral bars.

Unlike the axolotls, tiger salamanders metamorphose into terrestrial adults. Following hybridization, the *tigrinum* tendency to metamorphose was bred out by artificial selection.

With regards to albinism in lizards, records are not abundant. Hensley's survey of albinism in North American reptiles and amphibians included records of more than 100 snakes[4], but only one lizard. In recent years, herpetologists have reported aberrant reptiles and amphibians in the Herp Review Life History Notes, and this has been a convenient place for me to monitor "what has been found." I reviewed 100 issues from 1967 to the present for records of aberrant coloration and pattern and found 18 snakes and only three lizards.

It is possible that the incidence of albinism in lizards may be lower than that in snakes, but other explanations seem more likely. Most lizards are diurnal and low on the food chain. This combination makes them highly susceptible to predation, placing them in plain view for all predators to see. Fewer albinos may survive in the wild long enough to be collected. Furthermore, the absence of melanin combined with their diurnal life style make them susceptible to excessive ultraviolet radiation, which conceivably could have some negative survival value. Finally, if Valdosta, Georgia is typical, most young people with any interest in reptiles at all seem to concentrate on snakes, and don't even look for lizards.

HYPOPIGMENTATION AND PIGMENT LOSS THROUGH NATURAL SELECTION

A group of subterranean salamanders called blind salamanders occupy caves and underground streams in the limestone regions of the southern United States and Texas. I have had the opportunity to collect one of them, the Georgia blind salamander (*Haedeotriton wallaci*). Georgia blind salamanders are small, averaging 5.1–7.6 cm (2–3 in). A typical specimen is translucent pinkish-white, with skin so thin that viscera are discernible through the body wall. They have long red external gills, and the eyes are represented by black dots if they are present at all.

The first Georgia blind salamander collected was flushed up in an artesian well in Albany, Georgia. It was the only known specimen for many years, but they have now been found in some bat caves in northwest Florida. I easily observed several in the cave that I was led to by Bruce Means. Unfortunately, many of the habitats are in danger of being destroyed by quarrying and other activities, and some of the caves are still unprotected and accessible to vandals.

Even though they are white, blind cave salamanders are not albinos. Generations of life in the caves have made eyes and pigment unnecessary, and they have lost them by natural selection.

Another well-known example of pigment loss through natural selection is the speckled earless lizard (*Holbrookia maculata approximans*). Earless lizards have no visible ear openings, and several species are remarkably adapted for life in sandy soil. They have long legs and long toes for running on sand, and a head adapted for burrowing into the soft sand. When alarmed, they dive in headfirst and shimmy out of sight. Throughout most of the range they are strongly speckled on the dorsal surface. White Sands, NM, an area of dazzling white gypsum sand dunes near Alamagordo, is known for a nearly white race of this lizard. They are difficult to pick out from the background at best, and can disappear with a quick flurry of squirming.

ENDNOTES

1. Tokunaga, S.Y.O., and S. Akagishi. 1991. The Iwakuni shirohebis, a group of albino *Elaphe climacophora*. Herp Review. 22(4)
2. Shaw, C.E., and S. Campbell. 1974. Snakes of the American West. Alfred A. Knopf, New York.
3. Bechtel, H.B., and E. Bechtel. 1962. Heredity of albinism in the corn snake, *Elaphe guttata guttata*, demonstrated in captive breedings. Copeia. 2:436–437.
4. Hensley, M. 1959. Albinism in North American amphibians and reptiles, vol 1. Biological Series, Michigan State University, East Lansing:135–159
5. Groves, F. 1965. Further notes on albinism in the corn snake, *Elaphe guttata*. Copeia. 2:252.
6. Bechtel, H.B., and E. Bechtel. 1981. Albinism in the snake, *Elaphe obsoleta*. The Journal of Herpetology. 15 (4):397–402.
7. Bechtel, H.B., J.W. Nelson, and E. Bechtel. 1980. Histochemical demonstration of two types of albinism in San Diego gopher snakes (*Pituophis melanoleucus annectens*) by use of dopa reaction. Copeia 932–935.
8. Frost, S.K., F. Briggs, and G.M. Malacinski. 1984. A color atlas of pigment genes in the Mexican axolotl (*Ambystoma mexicanum*). Differentiation 26:182–188.

SNAKES

At the 1976 All Florida Herpetological Convention held in Gainesville, Florida, a friend who knew of my interest in abnormally colored snakes could hardly wait to tell me that Fred Antonio had a blue rattlesnake at the Santa Fe Community College. The Santa Fe Community College in Gainesville has a teaching zoo for potential zoo professionals, and Fred was the herpetologist overseeing that department. As soon as the formal lectures were finished, I hurried out to the zoo, not knowing what to expect. It was true, Fred did have a blue eastern diamondback rattlesnake, and it required no stretch of the imagination to call this snake "blue." It was normally patterned with white-bordered dark blue diamonds, against a lighter blue background. The eyes were black, and the venter gray-white. It was axanthic.

Axanthism is a hereditary defect of xanthophore pigment metabolism, resulting in absence or decreased amounts of red, yellow, and intermediate pteridine pigments. The defect involves the pteredine pigments, but has no effect on the carotenoids and other pigments that are contained in but not synthesized by the xanthophores. The word *axanthism* is derived from *xanthos*, Greek for yellow, and is translated literally as "without yellow."

This mutation affects only the xanthophores. Melanophores and iridophores function normally, and they interact to determine the color. Axanthic mutants of patterned species retain their patterns.

Axanthism in the Corn Snake

In the case of the corn snake, it has been firmly established that axanthism is caused by an autosomal recessive gene mutation. Axanthic corn snakes are patterned normally in shades of black and gray, with considerable individual variation in the quantity and quality of each of these colors. Specimens in which black blotches contrast sharply with a silvery gray background, though not colorful, are quite handsome.

From 1973 through 1977 we conducted a series of matings involving a wild-type female corn snake from Georgia and three wild-caught axanthic males from different gene pools in Florida. One was from near Immokalee in Hendry County, the second was from Moore Haven in Glades County, and the third was purchased from a Florida dealer with unknown collecting data.[1]

The series was started by mating an axanthic male with a wild type. The young from this mating were all pigmented normally and presumed to be heterozygous for axanthism. By 1975 the F_1's were sexually mature, and several test breedings were carried out. A mating of a female F_1 and an axanthic male produced five wild-type and nine axanthic young; a cross between a second female F_1 and an axanthic male produced seven wild-type and four axanthic young, and an F_1 cross produced six wild-type and two axanthic young. These ratios were consistent with inheritance by a recessive mutation. The breedings also indicated that the three wild-caught axanthic specimens were allelic, representing the independent recurrence of the same mutation in unrelated gene pools.

Axanthism may be interpreted in two ways. On the phenotypic level, it indicates the absence of the color yellow. On the functional level, it refers to absent or diminished xanthophore pigment metabolism. This can be a source of confusion, since many snakes have both red and yellow in their color mix.

Because of the predominance of red pigmentation in their pattern, corn snakes are also called red rat snakes. Their red pigment is synthesized by xanthophores, the same pigment cells that synthesize yellow. When xanthophores fail to function, neither red nor yellow are synthesized, but since the wild-type corn snakes are so overwhelmingly red, the absence of red in axanthic specimens is their most conspicuous feature. For this reason, they are called anerythristic (without red). While anerythrism is perfectly correct, I prefer to call all snakes with this mutation axanthic. This describes the mutation, and avoids stumbling over what to call tricolored kingsnakes with this mutation, since they clearly are both "without red" and "without yellow."

Axanthic snakes undergo ontogenetic color changes, and we have observed these in many corn snakes. As corn snakes reach sexual maturity, their red and orange colors become more intense. Axanthic corn snakes, basically black and gray at the time of hatching, also change colors ontogenetically, accumulating considerable yellow color as they age. This is most marked on the sides of the neck. Since it is generally considered that axanthic specimens are functionally incapable of synthesizing pteridine pigments of any color, the yellow is thought to result from accumulation of dietary carotenoids within the xanthophores. As for the axanthic diamondback, they too undergo ontogenetic color changes, with the blue becoming less intense.

Axanthism in the Texas Rat Snake

In 1981 we bred two Texas rat snakes (*Elaphe obsoleta lindheimeri*), and the clutch of 12 eggs contained two that clearly differed from typical hatchlings, which are grayish with brown blotches. The two stood out from the others by being patterned in black and white. One died, but the other was raised to over 121.9 cm (48 in) and the skin between her black scales remained chalky white. This was in sharp contrast to wild-type Texas rat snakes that are usually rather colorful because of the red, yellow, or orange skin between their scales. Phenotypically, she was axanthic, but she died before we could confirm this by breeding.

Axanthism in the Green Tree Python

Axanthism is an uncommon recurrent variant in the green tree python (*Chondropython viridis*). Green tree pythons are beautiful nonvenomous snakes from the jungles of New Guinea and northern Australia. Typical specimens are emerald green with a broken dorsal stripe of white or dull yellow and spots of similar color scattered over the body. Hatchlings are lemon yellow or golden orange with broken stripes and spots of purple and brown. The color change from juvenile to adult is completed in a few weeks. Adults average 91.5–121.9 cm (36–48 in), but giant specimens may reach 210 cm (7 ft). They are completely arboreal. In a small percentage, the green is replaced by a rich blue color.

Incidence

The incidence of axanthism in snakes is not known, but may be much greater than suspected. Since they are not as a rule conspicuous, the ones found by non-herpetologists are rarely recognized as something worth reporting.

The eastern mud snake (*Farancia abacura*) is a large snake common in the coastal plain of the southeastern United States from North Carolina south through Florida and west into Louisiana. Adults average 102–137 cm (40–54 in), with a record of 205.7 cm (81 in). They are shiny iridescent black on top with a pink or red underside extending as short lateral bars onto the lower few scale rows. They are secretive, nocturnal, and difficult to collect by conventional hunting methods. Occasionally one can be collected by turning over a partially submerged boat at the edge of a pond, or some similar situation, but most specimens are collected on highways, either dead or alive. Mud snakes are called horn snakes because of their stiff sharp tail. They feed almost exclusively on amphiumas (large legless salamanders), and they use the tail to maneuver the amphiumas into a better swallowing position. They also have a slightly disconcerting habit of pressing the sharp point of the tail against the hand when they are first picked up. They are not only nonpoisonous, but I believe it would be almost impossible to provoke one into biting. I have picked up many large ones and they have not even tried to bite in self-defense.

Axanthic specimens are black on top but deviate from the wild type by being white on the underside. While this color anomaly is astounding to herpetologists, who know what a mud snake should look like, a mostly black snake is not likely to attract the attention of a motorist travelling a rural road. An albino snake, on the other hand, might just bring the same motorist to a screeching stop, with the snake ending up at a zoo, college, or museum for identification. As a matter of fact, at least in my part of the country, most people who find an albino snake get at least one brief moment of fame in the local newspaper.

Axanthic mud snakes are apparently somewhat common. William Palmer, a herpetologist at the North Carolina State Museum of Natural History, furnished me with a prepublication draft of his state report on mud snakes in 1985. Of 120 North Carolina specimens observed, 8% had white rather than red belly and lateral bars. The underside of one adult male was red anteriorly and white posteriorly. All of the axanthic specimens were from the southeast part of the state.

Axanthic mud snakes have also been found in Georgia. Cruising back roads on warm evenings is one of our favorite pastimes, and we frequently find mud snakes at night. In 30 years we have found one axanthic specimen.

Axanthism is well known in the corn snake at this time, but this has not been the case for long. In 1980 Bette attempted to locate all known specimens by surveying published material and collections, and contacting individuals known to have collected them, who were aware of their existence, or who lived in south Florida.[2] At that time the herpetological community was not generally aware of the existence of this mutation, and the few known specimens were all from one area in Florida. In response to the survey, some respondents from south Florida, all of whom were quite familiar with the snakes of that area of Florida, responded by telling Bette in no uncertain terms that no such snake existed. She obtained a total of 16 records. Two were from Georgia and the others were from Florida.

Subsequent records demonstrate that axanthism in corn snakes is not limited to Florida and Georgia. A female axanthic specimen was collected in New Hanover County, South Carolina by R. Zuchowski, a herpetologist from Florida (personal communication, 1987). The snake was gravid when collected, and deposited four eggs. The hatchlings were all normally colored. She was mated the following year to an axanthic snake from a captive colony from the south Florida gene pool. Twelve hatchlings from this pairing were all axanthic, indicating that the South Carolina mutation was allelic with the known captive gene pool. We uncovered the gene for axanthism in a normally pigmented Louisiana specimen in the course of our breeding investigations, also allelic with the south Florida gene pool. Based on these records, axanthism is widespread within the range of the corn snake, but not equally abundant in all parts of the range. All of the Florida records were from the vicinity of Lake Okeechobee south to Homestead. The reason for the mutation being established in the south Florida gene pool is not known.

While it is generally assumed that individual albino snakes have a decreased chance of survival, it is not at all clear that the same can be said for axanthic snakes. They are not conspicuous, and probably escape detection rather than attract attention. Most of the axanthic corn snakes reported in the survey were adults, indicating that many do survive to adulthood.

Antonio and Barker[3] inventoried the known phenotypic aberrancies in the eastern diamondback rattlesnake. Among the aberrant specimens which included albinos, pattern anomalies, and snakes with two heads, two blue snakes were recorded, both from Florida. One was collected in Alachua County and the other in Duval County.

Nonallelic Axanthism

Nonallelic forms of axanthism have been discovered in the corn snake. The evidence for this was supplied by William Love, a herpetologist from Florida (personal communication, 1987). He collected a female axanthic corn snake in Lee County, Florida and in 1985 she was bred to a snake homozygous for axanthism, a cross expected to produce all axanthic young. To his surprise, the cross resulted in six wild types and two axanthic hatchlings. The same female was bred in 1986 to an albino not known to be heterozygous for axanthism, resulting in six wild-type and two axanthic hatchlings. In 1987 she was bred to an axanthic F_1 from her 1985 mating. This resulted in three wild-type and 14 axanthic hatchlings. It was concluded from these crosses that mutations at more than one locus can cause axanthism.

AMPHIBIANS

Though the incidence of axanthism in snakes is unknown, there is published evidence of the incidence in at least some frogs. The findings may have some relevance to the incidence in all reptiles and amphibians, since they share a common chromatophore system.

Blue (axanthic) frogs have been known to exist for years. Frogs are collected by the millions for research and educational purposes, and this has resulted in an opportunity to observe great numbers of individual frogs. Berns and Uhler[4] collected and tabulated data on the occurrence of blue frogs with the cooperation of major frog suppliers and a major biological supply house. Of a million ranid frogs screened in 1964, 33 were blue variants. A similar number screened in 1965 contained 36 blue variants, a ratio of approximately 1:30,000. This is generally analogous to the estimated incidence of albinism in various vertebrates. They found considerable variation in both quantity and quality of blue coloration in the frogs, and they found that the greatest concentrations of blue variants were in the north midwest United States, the northeast United States, and southeastern Canada.

Berns and Narayan[5] conducted a histochemical and ultrastructural analysis of the dermal chromatophores of two axanthic green frogs (*Rana clamitans*). Green frogs are medium-sized, green to greenish-brown with dorsal spots, averaging 5.7–8.9 cm (2¼–3½ in). The range includes much of eastern North America from southern Canada into Georgia and Alabama, and they are frequently abundant. Closely related frogs of the same species occur in the Gulf States. One of the frogs analyzed had a green mask with blue pigmentation extending from between the eyes to the anus. The other specimen was blue over the entire dorsal surface, but had green on the dorsal surfaces of the legs. In the blue areas, carotenoids were greatly reduced and pteridines were almost totally lacking. Carotenoids were present in abundance in the green skin and pteridines present in normal quantities.

Alvin Braswell, a herpetologist at the North Carolina Museum of Natural History, supplied me with information and a photograph of a blue Fowler's toad (*Bufo woodhousi fowleri*) from his back yard (personal communication). Fowler's toads are similar to other brown toads, but differ from others in their range by having an unspotted chest and three or more warts on each of the largest dark spots. They average 5.1–7.6 cm (2–3 in), and are common on the coastal plain from Massachusetts south into North Carolina and west as far as extreme eastern Oklahoma. The blue variant was found along with three wild types, all in the same general area and all about the same size category. This was the first blue toad that he had seen, and he has not found any since.

Axanthic axolotls have been described by Frost et al.[6] Wild-type larval axolotls are black on a yellow background, and adults are a mottled olive-green. Axanthic larvae are dark gray, and adults are charcoal gray. Axanthic mutants totally lack yellow pigmentation, and are similar in appearance to melanoids. The axanthic mutation was not reported until 1971, and healthy adults were difficult to rear at first.

Though axanthism is not as well known as albinism, mounting evidence indicates that this mutation, like albinism, is a widely distributed inherited color anomaly. Axanthism will most likely be recorded for every reptile and amphibian species if a sufficient number of individual specimens are observed.

ENDNOTES

1. Bechtel, H.B., and E. Bechtel. 1978. Heredity of pattern mutation in the corn snake, *Elaphe g. guttata*, demonstrated by captive breedings. Copeia 4:719–721.
2. Bechtel, E. 1980. Geographic distribution of two color mutants of the corn snake, *Elaphe guttata guttata*. Herp Rev 11:39–40.
3. Antonio, F.B., and J.B. Barker. 1983. An inventory of phenotypic aberrancies in the eastern diamondback rattlesnake (*Crotalus adamanteus*). Herp Review 14:108–109.
4. Berns, M.W., and L.D. Uhler. 1966. Blue frogs of the genus Rana. Herpetologica. 22:181–183.
5. Berns, M.W., and K.S. Narayan. 1970. An histochemical and ultrastructural analysis of the dermal chromatophores of the variant blue frog. J. Morph. 132:169–180.
6. Frost, S.K., F. Briggs, and G.M. Malacinski. 1984. A color atlas of pigment genes in the Mexican axolotl (*Ambystoma mexicanum*) Differentiation 26:182–188.

10

Leucism, Piebaldism, and Melanism

LEUCISM

Leucism in Snakes

Any large snake is enough to attract a crowd. If it happens also to be snow white with dark eyes, it is news. In 1955 the Staten Island Zoo obtained just such a snake on loan from her owner, Peter Ryhiner, a professional snake hunter. It was an adult Indian python (*Python molurus molurus*). An account of this remarkable snake was reported in the Zoological Society's 1956 annual report by Carl Kauffeld, curator of herpetology at the Staten Island Zoo.[1]

Indian pythons are giant snakes from India and Sri Lanka, with reliable reports of specimens exceeding 5.7 m (19 ft) and weighing 90 kg (200 lb). With rich brown blotches on a yellowish background, and their polished skin, they are striking even with normal coloration. They are powerful constrictors, eating mammals of any size they can handle. Large specimens can eat pigs and deer. In addition to their spectacular size and attractive color pattern, they are known for their pleasant demeanor, and have always been a staple of snake charmers. For many people, the only Indian python they have ever seen may have been draped around a seminude dancer at the circus side show. Even though they are powerful constrictors, and easily capable of killing a person, they are handled freely by performers.

A white python was rumored to exist in the region of East Pakistan where Mr. Ryhiner was collecting at the time, and it is easy to imagine why a professional snake hunter would get excited about this. His hunters sought and found that the creature actually existed, and were successful in capturing it. The snake was considered sacred and given the name of the goddess Serata. Before she was acquired by the zoo, Serata was exhibited in various places, and there is no doubt that she was the most publicized, the rarest, and the most valuable snake in the world. At one time or another she was featured in *Life* and *New Yorker* magazines.

Indian pythons are protected by Indian and international laws. The Burmese python (*Python m. bivittatus*) from the Malay Peninsula and southeast Asia is

71

essentially a darker phase of the Indian python, sharing all of its attributes, including its large size. Burmese pythons are available for purchase and pet stores sell thousands of them, frequently to customers who are attracted by their colors but have no idea how to care for them properly or how large they can grow, and they are usually so gentle that it is easy to forget that they can be dangerous. The result is an occasional newspaper report of some unfortunate person being killed by his pet python.

Serata was leucistic. Leucism is a hereditary chromatophore defect involving all chromatophores, and leucistic snakes have no functional melanophores or xanthophores, and very few iridophores. The term *leucistic* is derived from *leukos*, the Greek word for white. The word originated when knowledge of chromatophores was more rudimentary, and cannot even be found in the dictionary. It has, however, been used for years by herpetologists to identify these white mutants, and it serves in communication to distinguish them from other hypopigmented variants.

Very few leucistic snakes have been reported, and the incidence is unknown. The mutation is without doubt rare, but may be more common than suspected. Many leucistic snakes have probably been misidentified as albinos in the past. The few reported instances have been from widespread areas and included a number of different species.

Leucistic snakes of different species all look alike, differing only in size, scutellation, and other morphological traits. All are white with blue or darkly pigmented eyes.

Leucism was felt to be caused by a genetic mutation, but the mode of inheritance was not confirmed until 1981, when we had an opportunity to determine the genetics of leucism in the Texas rat snake.[2] Texas rat snakes are common in a range including southern Louisiana and the eastern half of Texas. They are large, averaging 120–180 cm (4–6 ft), with an occasional specimen exceeding 210 cm (7 ft). They are generally gray or yellowish with brownish or bluish-black blotches, but they are subject to considerable individual variation in color pattern. The skin between the scales may be yellowish, orange, or reddish, and this color often encroaches on the edges of the scales, with the result that some specimens are very attractive.

They are powerful constrictors, feeding primarily on birds and small mammals. They are good climbers and are often found in trees and rafters searching for birds, but they turn up in all situations. When blue jays and other birds spot one foraging, they frequently gather around and create a ruckus with frenzied calling and activity. An occasional snake can be collected by searching the area where the birds are making the disturbance.

Most rat snakes adapt well to captivity and are regarded as good cage snakes, since they become docile, are hardy, and are not finicky feeders. Texas rat snakes are hardy and adapt well but, for some reason, are quick tempered and bite repeatedly when threatened, even after years in captivity.

We obtained an adult white male with blue eyes on a breeding loan from the Houston Zoo in 1978, through the kindness of Hugh Quinn, Curator of Herpetology. It had been wild-caught as a juvenile and, to our knowledge, was the only known leucistic specimen. The snake died a few months after we received him, but mated with a wild type before dying. The mating resulted in five apparently fertile eggs, four of which hatched: three males and one female, all wild-type.

F_1's were crossed in 1981, the first year they were sexually mature. The mating resulted in 12 apparently fertile eggs. They all hatched, producing four leucistic and eight wild types. A similar cross the following year resulted in five hatchlings: one leucistic and four wild types. These results clearly indicated that the white gene is an autosomal recessive.

Leucistic Texas rat snakes have subsequently been bred by many individuals, all of them confirming the mode of inheritance, with the result that many individual specimens have been observed. Some of the leucistic specimens have conspicuously enlarged or protuberant eyeballs. Since this problem has not been associated with the wild types, it is apparently associated in some way with the leucism mutation, but the nature of the association has not been determined. Aside from color (and the occasional optic problem) leucistic specimens have no other abnormalities. Most of them are true to form, assuming a defensive posture, vibrating their tail, and striking and biting at every imagined threat.

A number of leucistic snakes have been brought to my attention, but one stands out because of the species involved. An immature white female eastern diamondback rattlesnake was found by road workers and obtained by Bill Love, a herpetologist and naturalist from Florida. The snake attained a very respectable size, but all attempts to breed her failed. During her life, she achieved considerable notoriety among herpetologists throughout the country since no one had ever seen anything like it, and no leucistic diamondbacks have surfaced since.

Leucism in Alligators

The New Orleans Audubon Park Zoo displays leucistic American alligators. Alligators range from east Texas eastward through Florida and northward into North Carolina and southern Arkansas. Adults average 150 cm (5 ft) or more, but can attain huge proportions. The record is 5.84 m (19 ft 2 in). Young alligators are black with bold yellowish crossbands. While the general coloration of adults is black, traces of the juvenile markings may persist. The leucistic alligators were white with dark eyes when discovered in a nest in Louisiana. They have developed a few dark spots with age, but are still striking in appearance.

Alligators are carnivorous and feed on any animal that they can capture. Large adults can kill large animals, but even large specimens feed mostly on smaller prey such as fish, turtles, snakes, waterfowl, and small mammals. Their reputation for eating dogs is exaggerated, but any small or medium-size animal that happens to swim and make a splash in water occupied by alligators is apt to attract the attention of one. Even though unprovoked attacks on man are rare, "Don't Feed the Alligators" warnings should be heeded. There have been fatalities, and many fatal alligator attacks on people are by alligators that have become accustomed to hanging around boat docks waiting for a handout.

Large populations live in the Okefenokee Swamp of Georgia and the Everglades National Park in Florida, where they have been protected for many years. They fascinate people because of their large size and prehistoric appearance, and visitors to these refuges seem to find the trip worthwhile if they get to see some of these primitive-appearing monsters in the wild. A large adult, seen up close, is an impressive sight.

Much of the alligator's original range has been infringed upon by development, and some has been made unusable by habitat alterations. In addition, they were hunted for their hides and even killed maliciously until, by 1967, their populations were so depleted that the species was declared endangered. With protection and proper management, populations have recovered to the point that controlled hunting has been resumed in several states. In fact, alligator meat has begun to appear on restaurant menus. This is hardly a cause for rejoicing, however, because the same circumstances that got them into trouble in the first place still exist, and are getting worse as the population continues to increase and more land is developed. Because people like to live near water for fishing, boating, and other recreation, contact with alligators is inevitable. People and alligators will have to live with each other if the alligator is to survive.

They are popular zoo attractions, and most zoos display them not only to give people a chance to see one, but also for educational purposes. The white alligators have proved to be excellent ambassadors for creating interest in and good will towards alligators, and they have been lent to several other zoos for this purpose.

Leucism in Axolotls

The most widely known leucism in amphibians is the white neotenic Mexican axolotl. The pigment genes in this species have been discussed by Frost et al.[3] The white gene appeared in laboratory stocks of axolotls early in this century.

Leucistic larvae are white instead of the typical black on yellow background. The adults are white to almost black instead of the normal mottled dark olive-green. The white mutants, with their prominent vascular external gills, are quite arresting. Leucism in the axolotl is also due to an autosomal recessive gene mutation, and great numbers are bred for research. Leucistic specimens have no visible pigment in the skin from larval stage up to about the time of sexual maturity. At or near sexual maturity, some specimens acquire a degree of pigmentation. This is the least understood of the inherited color defects in the axolotl colonies, and the tendency of some leucistic axolotls to repigment is not understood, since they are homozygous for the recessive white gene.

Basis of Leucism

As previously noted, microscopic examination of leucistic skin reveals no visible melanophores or xanthophores, and only a few iridophores. The manner in which the organism reads and processes the information on the mutated gene is unclear, but experimental evidence gained from axolotls indicates that the defect is within the white skin itself. In albinism and axanthism, the defect is inherent to the chromatophores themselves. In these two color defects, the chromatophores are present but nonfunctioning. If normal chromatoblasts are transplanted into albino or axanthic skin, normal pigment cells establish themselves and synthesize their respective pigments. This is not the case in leucism. Evidence indicates that the tissue environment of the white skin is defective in some way and cannot support pigment cells. The exact nature of the defect is undetermined.

Leucism, though rare, is a widespread mutation of reptiles and amphibians. Like albinism, it will probably be reported in all species when a sufficient number of individuals are observed.

PIEBALDISM

Piebald is defined as spotted or patched, especially in black and white. The white patches may range from a few small ones to extensive areas involving most of the body surface. In piebald animals, the sharply demarcated snow-white patches stand out in sharp contrast to the surrounding pigmented skin.

Piebald snakes have been reported. After Howard Gloyd published a paper on aberrant snakes[4] and gained some reputation for his interest in variants, friends and correspondents began to send him their unusual specimens. Of the hundreds of prairie rattlesnakes that he was able to observe, Gloyd described one piebald specimen collected in South Dakota.[5] It exhibited an absence of pigment on the posterior part of the body and tail, and a few white scales on both sides at mid-body. The large depigmented areas on the body began on the two lowest scale rows and extended up onto the sides. The involved areas were white with no traces of any other pigment. The remainder of the dorsal color was pale olive-brown, with the darker brown pigment irregularly clumped without any approach to the formation of symmetrical blotches typical of the species.

The prairie rattlesnake (*Crotalus v. viridis*) described by Gloyd was similar in appearance to a number of hypopigmented conditions that I occasionally see in my practice of dermatology: piebaldism, vitiligo, and postinflammatory leukoderma. Piebaldism in man is a congenital absence of pigment in certain parts of the body only. It is transmitted as a dominant Mendelian characteristic with complete penetration. There are three main types, each with slightly different manifestations.

Vitiligo is also manifested by depigmented white patches surrounded by normal skin, but it is ontogenetic (acquired during life). It may be associated with ocular disturbances, and the incidence is increased with several systemic conditions. The cause is unknown, though patients with vitiligo often have relatives with the same condition.

Postinflammatory leukoderma is manifested by areas of depigmentation resulting from dermatitis. Allergic contact dermatitis, leprosy, and other conditions are frequent causes. It is possible that some of the so-called piebaldism in reptiles and amphibians may prove to be postinflammatory leukoderma when more is known.

Two instances of partial pigment loss involving Burmese pythons have come to my attention. Steve Barten of Mundelein, Illinois, a veterinarian with an interest in herpetology, reported an unusual occurrence of ontogenetic color loss in a captive specimen.[6] A normally pigmented hatchling was purchased from a breeder and remained normal for almost two years. Then, in a brief period of one to two months the color faded until the snake was almost pure white with no trace of pattern, and a few remaining dark patches on the neck and the top of the head. Nothing was known of the ancestry of the snake, no skin disease preceded the pigment loss, and there is no suspected cause of this remarkable event.

A somewhat similar occurrence was related by Tom Weidner, a herpetologist from Des Moines, Iowa (personal communication, 1993). Over a short period of time a normally pigmented Burmese python lost all pigment except scattered lacy dark markings along the dorsal and lateral areas. Nothing to account for this was known in this case either.

Information regarding the possible genetics of piebaldism in a corn snake was supplied by Julian Cowles, a herpetologist from Tucson, Arizona (personal communication, 1992). He acquired a female corn snake with scattered white patches the length of the body. She was wild-caught in Florida. When she was mated with a wild type, the offspring (F_1 generation) were also wild types. An F_1 was bred back to the piebald mother, and all of the offspring were also wild types. At about three years, one of the wild-type offspring developed scattered white patches. The patches were indistinct for several sheds and then took on the appearance of spontaneous scars. Finally, the pigment disappeared completely, leaving large white patches. This clearly suggests a hereditary basis for piebaldism in the corn snake, with delayed onset of the manifestation, but more investigation is needed before drawing any firm conclusions.

MELANISM

Melanism in Snakes

Melanistic snakes are black variants of snakes that are ordinarily characterized by a color pattern. Melanism is the phenotypic opposite of leucism.

A form of ontogenetic melanism is normal in the blacksnake racer (*Coluber constrictor*) and some other species. The range of blacksnake racers includes most of the eastern United States from southern Maine through Florida. They are nonpoisonous and visually oriented, and active during the daylight hours. They are very omnivorous, eating small rodents, birds, frogs, lizards, and even other snakes. When approached, they race for cover and are difficult to catch, but they stand their ground and defend themselves if cornered. Adults average 91–152 cm (30–60 in). The various subspecies are quite similar to one another. In fact the southern black racer (*Coluber c. priapus*), found from southern North Carolina south to southern Florida, differs from the northern race only in internal anatomical differences. Newly-hatched racers are gray or bluish gray with dark blotches. As they mature, the pattern fades and their color darkens. By 76.2 cm (30 in) most specimens are satiny black above and below, with some white on the chin. Young blacksnake racers are a source of confusion to people who are not familiar with this ontogenetic color change. Nearly every summer, otherwise knowledgeable people bring immature blacksnake racers to me for identification. They never associate the little spotted snakes with the coal black ones that they are accustomed to encountering.

Melanism is a persistent variant in the eastern hognose snake (*Heterodon platyrhinos*) and also in a few other American snakes. Eastern hognose snakes occur from New Hampshire into Florida and west into South Dakota and Texas, preferring sandy areas within this range. An average adult is 51–84 cm (20–33 in), but the record is 115.6 cm (45½ in). They are named for their upturned snout, and their color patterns are so diverse that generalization is difficult. A typical specimen may be yellowish or tan, with dark blotches. However, other colors, such as red or gray, may predominate, and occasional specimens have different color patterns on either end of the body. Coal black phases occur in all parts of the range, and are quite common in south Georgia. Herpetologists who live within the range of these snakes and have hatched clutches of eggs generally agree that all are hatched with a color pattern, which indicates that the black phases become black ontogenetically.

Hognose snakes are generally most abundant where toads are also abundant, since toads are their preferred food. In captivity, many will accept only toads.

Hognose snakes are also called puff adders, spreading adders, blowing vipers and other names because they hiss, spread their neck into a cobra-like hood, and inflate their body with air when threatened. If the threat persists, they roll on their backs, open the mouth widely with the tongue dragging on the ground, disgorge their most recent meal, have a few convulsions, and lie still. They can be picked up like a limp rope. However, if they are righted, they promptly flop over on their back again, evidently under the impression that a dead snake should be on its back. When the threat is gone, the "dead snake" lifts its head, looks around to be sure the threat is gone, rolls over on its belly, and crawls off. Captive specimens almost never play dead after becoming adapted to cage life. Because of their alarming displays, combined with the fact that they are heavy-bodied, they are frequently assumed to be poisonous, and many are senselessly killed. They are not only nonpoisonous, but they rarely bite even when first picked up.

The closely related southern hognose snakes (*Heterodon simus*) are found in the southeastern United States from North Carolina south through most of Florida and west into southern Mississippi, with a range overlapping that of the eastern hognose. They are slightly smaller, averaging 36–51 cm (14–20 in), and are consistently light chocolate brown with darker brown blotches. There is little individual variation in color pattern, and melanism is not known to occur. This seems peculiar in light of the extremely variable pattern and frequency of melanism in the other species. They are easily confused with the eastern hognose snake, but have a more sharply upturned snout.

The eastern massasauga (*Sistrurus catenatus*) is another snake known for melanism. Massasaugas are small rattlesnakes with a range extending from central New York and southern Ontario to Iowa and Missouri, but they are no longer found in most of the original range due to destruction and alteration of their habitat. Adults average 51–76 cm (20–30 in). They are typically gray or brownish with large black or dark brown blotches, but it has been known for years that some adults are jet black, both above and below.

Conant[7] reported a substantial colony near Mt. Victory, Hardin County, Ohio, composed almost entirely of melanistic individuals. Of the snakes collected, all of the adults were black and all juveniles spotted, and the farmers in the vicinity reported that spotted adults were rare or absent. Black females from the vicinity invariably gave birth to spotted young. Black specimens were not common in other localities in Ohio.

I had an opportunity to look for massasaugas in Ohio in 1957. Following distribution maps from Conant's "The Reptiles of Ohio," I went to Hardin County. The habitat had been greatly degraded since 1938 when Roger Conant wrote his field guide, and did not appear promising. However, in an afternoon of searching the most likely looking spots, I found one snake, a jet black massasauga, which I photographed and sent on its way.

The timber rattlesnake is also known for black variants. Every melanistic specimen that I observed had some visible pattern showing through, but coal black specimens are known.

Sporadic black variants of other snakes appear from time to time in species not known for melanistic variants. Gloyd[8] recounted an interesting, but nearly tragic event involving a black coral snake in Texas. A lady who was somewhat familiar with snakes was walking with her daughter when they came upon a slender black snake. The young girl put her foot on the snake and the lady picked it up. Even when it managed to bite her on a finger, she was not alarmed, because she knew no local venomous snakes were black. However, she developed pain in the affected extremity and summoned a physician. Though she subsequently developed symptoms of severe envenomation, she recovered, even though this experience took place before coral snake antivenin was developed.

Eastern garter snakes (*Thamnophis sirtalis*) are widely known for melanistic variants. They are nonpoisonous snakes with a range extending from southern Canada to the Gulf of Mexico, and west into Minnesota and Texas. Adults average 46–66 cm (18–26 in), but have been known to attain a length of 123.8 cm (48¾ in). They are variable in color pattern, but are typically dark brown, green, or olive, with three yellowish longitudinal stripes. Most of them have a double row of alternating black spots between the stripes, and the dark spots in some specimens form a checkered pattern. Coal-black specimens with a white throat occur occasionally, and with some frequency in Ohio near the shores of Lake Erie, where as many as one third of the population in one point in southern Ontario are melanistic.

Garter snakes are frequently abundant in urban areas and are often the first snake collected by young people just learning about herpetology. They are also rather easy to cater to in captivity since they eat food that is easy to find: frogs, toads, salamanders, fish, tadpoles, and earthworms.

Between 1933 and 1937 Blanchard and Blanchard[9] conducted a series of controlled breedings to determine the genetics of melanism. When black to black were bred, all of the offspring were black. When black was bred to striped, all of the offspring were striped. However, when striped F_2's were bred with each other, both black and striped appeared, with ratios indicating that melanism in the garter snake is caused by an autosomal recessive gene mutation.

The Blanchards had made a previous attempt in 1923 to demonstrate the genetics of melanism in garter snakes by keeping a black male and two striped females in the same enclosure during the winter and spring. No melanistic specimens resulted when they bred F_2's from this enclosure, even though they had significant numbers of young. This was puzzling until it was concluded that the two females had been fertilized in the fall before they were placed in the enclosure with the black male. Until then it was not generally known that garter snakes are sometimes fall breeders.

Melanistic garter snakes are black at birth. Black hognose snakes and massasaugas are patterned at birth and become black ontogenetically. There is some fundamental genetic or developmental difference between those that are born black and those that become black ontogenetically, but further investigation will be needed to determine what the difference is.

No published survey of melanism in snakes has been done. However, melanistic specimens of various species continue to be reported, and melanism is probably more common than reports indicate. The only person who would know that a melanistic snake is unusual would have to be familiar with the wild type, so a black variant is unlikely to attract the attention of anyone other than a herpetologist.

Melanism in Lizards

Melanistic pearl lizards (*Lacerta lepida pater*) originating in Morocco have been reported by Langerwerf.[10] Pearl lizards belong to a large and colorful family of lizards from Europe, Asia, and Africa known as wall and sand lizards. They are a subspecies of the ocellated green lizard (*Lacerta lepida*).

In a captive breeding colony, maintained as a community with several males and females, out of hundreds of hatchlings, one clutch of 22 eggs hatched one melanistic specimen and 21 wild types. From this colony several other females produced melanistic young: 1 in 25; 3 in 25; and 4 in 28. One of the melanistic females was raised to maturity and mated with a wild type resulting in 17 hatchlings, all wild types. The supposition was that the melanism is due to an autosomal recessive gene, and the breeding colony contained several females and at least one male heterozygous for the mutation.

Melanism in Amphibians

Melanoid axolotls are well known.[3] Melanism in axolotls is caused by an autosomal recessive gene mutation. The larval forms are black with very little of the yellow background that the wild types have, and they become velvety black adults. Microscopic examination of the skin reveals increased melanophores and no iridophores. Xanthophores are diminished in numbers.

Melanism has been reported also in other salamanders, such as the spotted salamander (*Ambystoma maculatum*). Spotted salamanders are medium-sized salamanders averaging 15–20 cm (7–8¼ in), occurring from southern Canada southward through the eastern half of the United States and east Texas. They are ordinarily black or bluish black with an irregular row of yellow or orange spots from the head to the tip of the tail. I have found them in moist soil beneath logs, but the easiest way to find them is at their breeding sites. They are spring breeders and migrate in great numbers to woodland ponds starting with spring rains, at which time they are easy to find. One of the thrills of field herpetology is to witness a pond with breeding pairs of these lovely amphibians.

Easterla[11] reported finding two melanistic specimens in Clay County, Arkansas. They lacked dorsal spots, but one possessed several tiny light-colored flecks. Eleven wild types were associated with the melanistic individuals, and several hundred collected at nearby sites within the next three days were all wild types. The melanistic specimens lacked the dorsal spots, but one possessed several tiny light-colored flecks.

ENDNOTES

1. Kauffeld, C. 1956. The reptile department in 1955. Annual Report-1955 Staten Island Zoological Society Inc. 23:5–6.
2. Bechtel, H.B., and E. Bechtel. 1985. Genetics of color mutations in the snake, *Elaphe obsoleta*. Journal of Heredity. 76:7–11.
3. Frost, S.K., F. Briggs, and G.M. Malacnski. 1984. A color atlas of pigment genes in the Mexican axolotl (*Ambystoma mexicanum*). Differentiation. 26:182–188.
4. Gloyd, H.K. 1935. Some aberrant color patterns in snakes. Papers Mich. Academy Sci., Arts and Letters 20:661–668.
5. Gloyd, H.K. 1958. Aberrations in the color patterns of some crotalid snakes. Bulletin of the Chicago Academy Sciences. 10:185–195.
6. Barten, S., F. Frye, R. Evans, and P. Ihrke. 1985. *Python molurus bivittatus* (Burmese python). Herp Review. 16(2):57.
7. Conant, R. 1951. The Reptiles of Ohio. Univ. Notre Dame Press, 2nd ed.
8. Gloyd, H.K. 1938. A case of poisoning from the bite of a black coral snake. Herpetologica 1:121–124.
9. Blanchard, F.N., and F.C. Blanchard. 1941. The inheritance of melanism in the garter snake *Thamnophis sirtalis sirtalis* (Linnaeus) and some evidence of effective autumn mating. Pap. Mich. Acad. Sci. Arts Lett. 26:177–193.
10. Langerwerf, B.K. 1981. Nigrinos bei der nachzucht von, *Lacerta lepida pater*. Herpetofauna 12:21–22.
11. Easterla, D.A. 1968. Melanistic spotted salamanders in northeast Arkansas. Herpetologica. 24:330–331.

11
Anomalous Patterns

The patterns of reptiles and amphibians are normally consistent enough to serve as identification characters, but many people see only what they expect or want to see. Valdosta is a south Georgia town of 40,000 plopped down in what was formerly prime diamondback rattlesnake habitat, and some diamondbacks still live here. I have dipped one from a motel swimming pool several blocks from the city hall, have rescued many from patios and carports, and even collected a large one from a city street while driving home from hospital rounds, all within the city limits. Families transferred here from large cities of the northeast have often heard about our bugs, snakes, and alligators even before they move here, and they arrive with apprehensions. As resident naturalist, I get many calls about snakes. I also get calls concerning insects, spiders, bats, hawks, and owls, since people think that anyone who likes snakes must also likes nature's other outcasts. In my case they are right, but the most urgent calls are about snakes. After the caller calms down, and I ask what the snake looks like, he or she describes the pattern. If the description is accurate, and it frequently isn't, I can often identify it without seeing it and put the person's mind at ease. The truth is that many people are poor observers at best, and even worse in the excitement of finding a snake on the patio. They see what they expect to see: the dreaded rattlesnake. Every snake is a rattlesnake, and every pattern a diamond. They see diamonds in black snakes with yellow rings, and occasionally in snakes with no pattern at all. After hanging up from one call, Bette commented, "How would you like to have her as a witness at a trial?"

Herpetologists can often identify a snake before getting close enough to see the pattern, from its size and shape, or even the way it is holding its head, but for most people, snakes are long and legless and all look alike except for pattern. If people would learn to recognize them, they could be more comfortable around snakes.

While it is safe to reassure people that patterns are reliable identification characters, every herpetologist knows that rare reptiles and amphibians with anomalous patterns occur, some almost defying identification. The genetic and developmental aspects of pattern formation are complicated and not totally understood, but the power of genes is understood. They control every step of pattern formation from the time the egg is fertilized until the embryo is fully developed. Mutant genes that can adversely affect pattern formation lurk in every gene pool. Furthermore, nutritional status, disease, and incubation temperature during early embryo development can also result in abnormal patterns. They may take any form. Some fall into regularly recurring categories, striping for example. Others are random or at any rate very uncommon, often known to science by only a specimen or two.

```
┌─────────────────────────────────────────────────────────────────┐
│  SNAKES                                                           │
└─────────────────────────────────────────────────────────────────┘
```

```
┌─────────────────────────────────────────────────────────────────┐
│  Striping                                                         │
└─────────────────────────────────────────────────────────────────┘
```

Striped variants of snakes that are ordinarily blotched, ringed, banded, or marked with diamonds are well known, and striping of all or part of the body is probably a more common variant than would be suspected from casual collecting. Klauber attributed the phenomenon to an aberration in the genic mechanism causing a peculiar 90° rotation of the pattern, transforming blotches or rings into longitudinal stripes. Based on the appearance of many striped variants, this explanation is tenable, but does not explain the underlying developmental mechanisms.

The most widely known example of striping is the California kingsnake (*Lampropeltis getula californiae*), a nonpoisonous variety with a range extending from Oregon south into Baja California and eastward into Arizona, Nevada, and western Colorado. California kingsnakes average 91.4–208.3 cm (36–82 in). They occupy a variety of habitats within their large range and feed on a variety of small mammals and birds, lizards, frogs, and snakes, including rattlers. Their scales are smooth and polished-looking. Throughout most of the range the pattern is composed of yellow to white rings on a brown to black background. In parts of southern California, however, the ringed pattern is replaced by a yellow to white longitudinal stripe in about 40% of the snakes.

For years the ringed and striped forms were considered separate species. The ringed phase was called Boyle's kingsnake (*Lampropeltis getulus boylii*). Based on similar scale counts and other morphological characters, it was thought that they could be pattern variations of the same species, but the confusion was cleared up by hatching two broods, one from a mother of each form.[1] Each brood contained young of both pattern phases, demonstrating that both are merely different pattern phases of the same species. The broods were hatched in 1936 by Robert Hoard of the San Diego Zoological Society. It is astonishing, and gives an idea of how far snake husbandry has progressed, that these two broods were the first snakes ever successfully hatched at the San Diego Zoo.

Even after it was determined that the striped and ringed forms were the same species, the genetics remained unclear. Zweifel[2] finally determined the genetics of striping in an analysis based on 14 crosses performed in the laboratory among five male and five female snakes that produced 90 young. He demonstrated that the ubiquitous ringed pattern is recessive to the striped morph. The degree of dominance (purity of striping) appears to be influenced by modifiers.

California kingsnakes exhibit considerable pattern diversity and not all specimens are pure striped or ringed morphs. In the area in which striped specimens are most common, broken striped specimens are also frequent. This type includes snakes with numerous breaks in the dorsal stripe, and the extreme specimens have a row of spots. In others, some of the stripe segments appear to be turned at an angle or even perpendicular to the body axis. A common pattern in the southern California coastal area is the mixed pattern. This pattern is intermediate between broken stripe and ringed. One morph known only from Los Angeles County is basically ringed, but the ventral surface is wholly dark and the dorsal surface has a dusky suffusion, greatly dulling the yellow to white rings.

A variant from Orange County and coastal Los Angeles County has a definite though irregular stripe and lateral markings that look like interrupted cross-bands and stripes. Zweifel reported one female of this morph collected from Long Beach that was gravid when captured and produced five typical ringed young and two virtually indistinguishable from the mother. On this basis, he suggested a third allele at the ring-stripe locus.

Striping is also a known variant in gopher snakes. Gopher snakes are members of a large genus (*Pituophis*) of nonpoisonous snakes with ten recognized subspecies occupying a variety of habitats from New Jersey and Florida on the east coast to California on the Pacific coast, including parts of Mexico on the south and Canada on the north. They are large, handsome snakes, usually boldly marked, and are among America's largest species. All are powerful constrictors.

With the exception of the black pine snake (*Pituophis melanoleucus lodingi*) of southwestern Alabama and extreme eastern Louisiana, all gopher snakes are blotched. Adult black pine snakes are plain black above and below, but immature specimens of even this race display at least traces of blotches. They average 122–163 cm (48–64 in) in length.

The largest snake of the genus is the bullsnake (*Pituophis melanoleucus sayi*), which has been known to attain a length of 254 cm (100 in), though the average size is 127–183 cm (50–72 in). Bullsnakes are associated with the plains and prairies in an extensive range extending from the Rockies in the west into western Indiana, including parts of southern Canada and northern Mexico. They are ordinarily yellowish with black or brown blotches, but those from the arid parts of the west are lighter in color. When threatened they hiss loudly, vibrate their tails, and wave their extended tongue up and down. It is all bluff, but many people are alarmed by their menacing actions and kill them. Many are also killed by speeding autos. They are big and noted for eating rodents, and enlightened ranchers and farmers either tolerate or actually protect them on their property in many places.

In some areas of California an occasional gopher snake has the blotched pattern replaced by longitudinal stripes on either side of the mid-dorsal line. Reimer[3] examined a series of eight striped and five striped-blotched specimens from California. He found considerable variation in the nature and completeness of the striping, and some with a combination of blotches and striping, but all were clearly striped instead of blotched. The striped variants differ additionally from the blotched morphs by having an unmarked venter. The blotched morphs have a plain venter with small black squares scattered sparsely over the abdomen, while the venter of striped morphs is unmarked tan or cream, with dark pigment at the tip of each ventral plate where these join the lowest row of dorsal scales. All but one of the striped specimens were from the vicinity of San Francisco, in the range of the Pacific gopher snake (*Pituophis melanoleucus catenifer*), a subspecies ranging from western Oregon south to Santa Barbara County, California. Pacific gopher snakes are marked with dark brown or black blotches, separated from each other and an adjacent lateral series by a background color suffused with gray. Reimer speculated that the striping resulted from some genic mechanism.

My wife and Terry Whitecar, a herpetologist from Tarpon Springs, Florida, determined the genetics of striping in gopher snakes in an analysis based on four blotched × blotched crosses, three blotched × striped crosses, and two striped × striped crosses.[4] All blotched × blotched crosses produced only blotched offspring. One blotch × striped cross produced six blotched and six striped offspring. The second blotch × striped cross produced four blotched and four striped offspring, and the third produced one blotched and five striped offspring. One striped × striped cross produced three striped and no blotched offspring, and the other produced three blotched and 10 striped offspring. The results were unanticipated. Even though the striped morphs are rare, the widespread blotched pattern is recessive to it.

Until recently, striping was not a known variant of the corn snake. The presence of a gene for striping was discovered in a hatchling female corn snake from Hillsborough County, Florida that we obtained in 1972.[5] Her pattern deviated from the normal blotched pattern in several ways, which is why we obtained her. She had an unmarked venter, and the dorsal pattern was atypical in several ways. The first twelve blotches were united by lateral prongs, and there were no blotches on the lowest scale rows.

A series of matings was undertaken to determine if this pattern anomaly was caused by mutation. A mating with a wild type in 1975 resulted in 16 wild-type hatchlings. Two pairs of the F_1 generation were retained for further breeding. In 1977 an F_1 was back-crossed with the original female, resulting in 16 hatchlings: five wild types and 11 with pattern anomalies. A cross between two F_1's the same year resulted in seven wild types and one with a pattern anomaly. The matings clearly indicated that the pattern anomaly was caused by an autosomal recessive gene mutation. All 12 hatchlings with pattern anomalies were stigmatized with an absence of ventral markings and the atypical dorsal markings of the original female. However, in some, the changes led to striping on parts of the body. The expression of the genotype proved to be variable. Snakes homozygous for this mutation (in subsequent matings) have included specimens with longitudinal stripes the entire length of the body.

The prairie kingsnake (*Lampropeltis c. calligaster*), with an extensive range in middle America, is a species not known for consistent striped variants. Prairie king snakes are medium sized, averaging 76–107 cm (30–42 in), ordinarily patterned with brownish to greenish blotches on a gray to tan background. They have the smooth and polished surface typical of kingsnakes. Like all kingsnakes, they are powerful constrictors and include snakes in their diet, as well as small rodents, lizards, frogs, and birds. The pattern of some older specimens becomes obscure, and they develop four dusky longitudinal stripes.

To determine the incidence of striping in this species, Stanley Dyrkacz, a herpetologist from Kansas, surveyed museum specimens and literature reports for records.[6] Ten specimens were reported. Those with prominent dorsal stripes were patterned similarly, and some were hatchlings when reported. The evidence from this survey is that there is a genetic mutation causing striping in some prairie kingsnakes, and it also indicates that striping may be a more frequent variant than suspected. In one case, a clutch of 12 eggs produced three striped hatchlings. In another, a clutch of 13 eggs produced a single striped hatchling. In the third clutch, four of eight eggs hatched. Two had prominent dorsal stripes and two were wild types. In all three cases, the mothers were patterned normally. Of those examined, the ones with prominent dorsal stripes were patterned in similar fashion with two longitudinal stripes 2–4 scales wide, 1–2 scales on either side of the mid-dorsal line.

The American herpetologist, Howard Gloyd, from boyhood had an interest in rattlesnakes and other pit vipers, and they became the focus of his life's research. In the course of his career he examined numerous pit vipers, and published papers describing the anomalous ones, including some striped variants.[7,8] One in particular was a male striped northern copperhead snake collected in Jackson County, Missouri. Of the several hundreds of copperheads that he had the opportunity to examine, this was the only one with this anomaly.

The northern copperhead is a medium-sized venomous pit viper with a range extending from Massachusetts westward to Missouri and south into the hills of north Alabama and Georgia. Adults average 61–91 cm (2–3 ft), and they rarely exceed 120 cm (4 ft). A typical specimen has dark chestnut bands against a lighter brown background. Young copperhead snakes have a yellow tail which they waggle to lure frogs into striking distance. The dark bands are wide on the sides and, when viewed from above, create an hourglass pattern. Lying amid fallen leaves on the forest floor, copperheads are nearly invisible. They derive their name from their copper-colored head. They feed principally on mice, but eat other small vertebrates, and even insects. Rocky and abandoned farms and sawmills are excellent places to search for them.

Four other recognized varieties of copperhead snakes extend the range to the Florida Panhandle in the east to the Big Bend region of Texas in the west. They differ from the northern copperhead in the shades of brown and configuration of the bands. All fall in the same general size range, and all are readily recognized as copperheads. Over much of its range in the populous northeast, the copperhead is the most prevalent venomous snake, or even the only venomous one, and many people have copperheads as next-door neighbors, often without knowing it. As a result, the northern copperhead is responsible for more poisonous snakebites than any other snake. Fortunately, though painful, their bites are treatable.

Gloyd's striped variant possessed two more or less normal hourglass-shaped crossbands on the neck, but those on the remainder of the body up to the fourth from the last did not extend up to the midline but had coalesced into broad lateral stripes involving the five to seven lower scale rows. The stripes were darker at the upper borders and narrowly edged with white, causing the broad tan dorsal stripe to stand out. This striping in the snake clearly looked like what would be expected if the normal bands were rotated 90°.

Gloyd also reported a striped timber rattlesnake collected in Franklin County, Pennsylvania, in which the transverse bands were replaced by a seal-brown mid-dorsal stripe with a cream-colored border and similar stripes on each side. Nickerson and Mays[9] reported two timber rattlesnakes collected in Jo Daviess County, Illinois, with striping similar to Gloyd's specimen, but lacking the marginal light color of the stripes. Both had a mid-dorsal stripe and two similar lateral stripes running the length of the body. Both were collected no more than 200 yards apart and were approximately the same size and pattern, indicating that they may have been litter mates.

In some snakes with stripes replacing the normal pattern, the striping involves only the front half of the body. This has been noted especially with rattlesnakes, but it is also true with other snakes. Gloyd described a prairie rattlesnake with this type of striping. Prairie rattlesnakes are common rattlesnakes of the grasslands of the Great Plains, ranging from the Rockies eastward to western Iowa and from southern Canada into Mexico. They are medium-sized rattlesnakes, averaging 89–114 cm (35–45 in). They are ordinarily greenish gray or greenish brown, with dark brown white-bordered blotches.

Prairie rattlers overwinter in rocky outcrops and are sometimes very numerous at these hibernating sites, or at any rate were at one time. A. M. Jackley of Pierre, South Dakota, collected nearly 2500 in 1932 and 1933, and Gloyd arranged for all of the unusual specimens to be sent to him. In one specimen, the pigment that produces the blotches was arranged in two longitudinal stripes over the anterior part of the body.

Gloyd also described a Mojave rattlesnake (*Crotalus scutulatus*) with the striping of the anterior part of the body. Mojave rattlesnakes are gray or brownish with brown diamonds or hexagons. Their range extends from west Texas into southern Nevada and nearby California and south into Mexico. They are easily confused with the western diamondback rattlesnake which shares much of the same territory, but the black tail rings of the Mojave are much narrower than the white rings. Mojave rattlesnakes are not particularly large, averaging 61–91 cm (24–36 in), but they possess an unusually virulent venom, and are very dangerous.

Gloyd described a specimen in which the normal diamonds were replaced anteriorly by a broad mid-dorsal stripe. The snake was collected in Graham County, Arizona. Nickerson and Mays[9] also reported an Arizona specimen with the first six to eight dorsal blotches fused into a wide mid-dorsal stripe. It was collected in Pinal County, Arizona, and Nickerson stated that he had seen others with similar pattern and that fusion of the first two to three dorsal blotches is not uncommon in Mojave rattlesnakes from several Arizona counties.

In regard to striping, a western milksnake (*Lampropeltis doliata*) reported by Gelbach[10] is interesting in that the striping involved only the posterior part of the body. It was collected in Santa Fe County, New Mexico. The only subspecies found in that county is now reclassified *Lampropeltis triangulum celaenops*, and is called the New Mexico milksnake. New Mexico milksnakes are medium-sized snakes occupying a range largely confined to New Mexico. They average 36–63 cm (14–24¾ in). They are beautiful, typically patterned with reddish rings edged with black, separated by white or yellow. In the striped variant, the dorsal black-red-black bands or triads were replaced over most of the posterior half of the body by black longitudinal stripes bordered below by faint red stripes. The pattern anomaly was accompanied by abnormal scutellation, most notably 160 entire and 13 divided ventrals, and 21 entire and 21 divided subcaudals. In view of the fact that striping is not common in this species, and since there are associated scale anomalies, it is possible that this anomaly could result from stress during embryogenesis rather than some genetic defect.

Striping is a naturally occurring variant of many snakes, and there is ample evidence that it is genetically determined in a number of species. Specific knowledge of the embryology and developmental aspects of striping are lacking, however. It is interesting and puzzling that aberrant striping often involves only one end of the snake, and the fact that it can be either end only makes it more perplexing.

Since striping in the corn snake has been described only recently, it is worth noting that Gloyd described a striped variant of the great plains rat snake (*Elaphe guttata emoryi*) in 1935.[8] Great plains rat snakes, or Emory's rat snakes as they are also called, are a western subspecies of the corn snake. They range from western Illinois west into Colorado and New Mexico, and south through Texas into Mexico. They are typically light gray with dark gray, brown, or olive-brown blotches. The pattern is similar to that of the corn snake, including the spearpoint between the eyes, but they are far less colorful. A specimen from San Antonio, Texas, departed from the normal pattern by having the blotches of the dorsal series either partially or entirely divided along the mid-dorsal line, resulting in H-shaped figures and two longitudinal stripes in other areas.

Some striped variants appear to arise, not from a rotation of the pattern, but from elongation and merging of individual dorsal blotches. The resulting stripe in these variants often takes the form of an irregular dorsal stripe of the same color as the blotches.

Zig Zag

In some snakes normally possessing a single mid-dorsal series of blotches, the blotch halves on the two sides of the mid-dorsal line are asymmetrically spaced, resulting in a zig zag pattern. In extremely aberrant instances, the blotches are matched so poorly that they are connected by diagonal bars, each of which joins the posterior end of one blotch half and the anterior end of the next blotch half on the opposite side of the body. The result is a wavy or zig zag longitudinal stripe.

This anomaly has some genetic basis. Most snakes with this anomaly have only a portion of the dorsal pattern affected. However, Bill Love was able to produce a corn snake with the zig zagging involving nearly the entire dorsal pattern (personal communication, 1988). He started with a wild-caught snake with partial zig zagging and selected those with the greatest amount for each successive generation.

Patternless

Patternless morphs of normally patterned species have also been reported, and patternless copperheads have been known to herpetologists since at least 1959. Henry Fitch, an American herpetologist from the University of Kansas, in a 10-year study of 1279 copperhead snakes on a 590-acre tract in northeastern Kansas, reported five patternless specimens.[11] A wild-type female gave birth to four young, two wild-type females and two patternless males. A second wild-type female gave birth to two wild-type females, two wild-type males, and a patternless male. Two patternless males were collected during the study. The patternless specimens had the normal two-tone bands replaced by a uniform light brown color. The occurrence of all of these specimens from a small geographical area, and the birth of wild types and patternless specimens in the same litter, strongly suggest that a recessive mutation accounts for this. All of the specimens without pattern were males. This may be significant, but a larger series would be necessary to determine this.

Though lack of pattern in normally patterned species is uncommon, I have received slides of patternless eastern diamondback rattlesnakes, western diamondback rattlesnakes, and red diamondback rattlesnakes (*Crotalus ruber*). Based on the photographs, all are uniform brown and so similar that it would probably require scale counts to identify them.

Developmental aspects of patternlessness are not known, though a genetic mutation is evidently the underlying cause in at least some cases. The problem is more likely in the prepattern or the skin environment and not in the chromatophores themselves.

AMPHIBIANS: OTHER REPTILES

Color and pattern anomalies of amphibians and reptiles other than snakes are generally analogous to those seen in snakes. All share the same chromatophore types and similar mechanisms of pattern formation. Some salamanders, as do a number of snake species, have extremely polymorphic patterns.

Frogs

A patternless variant of the northern leopard frog (*Rana pipiens*) is known. Leopard frogs have an extensive range including parts of southern Canada and much of the northern portions of the United States. Wild types are brown or green with conspicuous dark spots on the sides and between the dorsolateral ridges, averaging 5.1–12.8 cm (2–5 in). They are the most well-known frog in much of their range. During the day they hide in the grass at the edge of the water. When approached they dive into the water, make a sharp turn, and disappear into the vegetation. They eat insects, and in turn are eaten by birds, raccoons, snakes, hawks and owls, and numerous other predators.

In parts of Minnesota and nearby states a small percentage are aberrant, with black spots reduced or absent, except for a spot behind each elbow. When they were first discovered, they were described as a new species (*Rana burnsi*), and they are still referred to as the Burnsi mutant.

However, Moore[12] was able to demonstrate in controlled breeding experiments that both morphs are different pattern phases of *Rana pipiens*. Furthermore, on the basis of his observations, the ubiquitous spotted pattern is recessive to the patternless morph. The differences between the two morphs are visible even in the tadpoles.

Though the patternless morph of the leopard frog is clearly dominant to the more abundant spotted form, the patternless morph is not common. In the areas that contain the most Burnsi mutants, unspotted frogs comprise about 0.1–10.3% of the population, and the ratio of the two morphs appears to be in equilibrium. This seems contradictory to common sense, but apparently the spotted and patternless morphs are equally adaptive. In this event, if the population is large, and it is with frogs, and no significant new alleles are formed by mutation, all genotypes should reproduce equally well with random mating.

Lizards

Patternless variants of lizards also occur. Eleven species of whiptails or race-runner lizards (*Cnemidophorus*) occur in the United States, ranging from coast to coast. All are diurnal and named for their long tails. Most species are striped, or marked with bars, spots, or checkers. However, many are very similar, and their patterns change with growth. It is often necessary to pick a specimen up and examine scales and pattern features closely for identification. Even picking them up is a problem. They are active, wary, fast, and very difficult to catch.

Marbled whiptails (*Cnemidophorus tigris marmoratus*) are common in arid sandy areas of the Chihuahuan Desert of west Texas and adjacent Mexico and New Mexico. They have a pronounced marbled dorsal pattern and a slight indication of dorsal striping, and average 20.3–30.5 cm (8–12 in). A population in west Texas, first found in 1963, contains an unusual number of patternless individuals.[13] The patternless individuals are uniform brownish-gray dorsally and white on the underside, and include both sexes. Of 17 specimens collected in a small area, four were patternless.

ENVIRONMENTALLY CAUSED PATTERN ANOMALIES

Not every anomalous pattern has a genetic basis. Incubation temperatures both higher and lower than optimum have been demonstrated to cause abnormal patterns in snakes, turtles, and alligators.

Indian and Burmese pythons differ from most snakes in that they brood their eggs, and are able to maintain an incubation temperature higher than the surrounding temperature. A brooding female can generate heat and maintain an incubation temperature of 32–33°C, which is considered the optimum incubation temperature for the species. The heat is generated by frequent intermittent muscle contractions. Brooding females lie coiled around the clutch in this fashion for 60 days or more. Vinegar[14] incubated eggs at optimum and below optimum temperatures. He found that eggs developed normally at 30.5°C, abnormally at 27.5°C, and did not develop at 23°C. The abnormalities fell into two categories: pattern anomalies and abnormalities of the vertebral column. The most conspicuous pattern anomalies were a tendency for the light brown background color to appear as light areas in the centers of blotches and dorsolateral stripe formation in the neck and tail regions.

The effects of temperature and carbon dioxide levels during incubation were studied in the red-eared turtle (*Trachemys scripta elegans*).[15] Red-eared turtles occur in ponds and other bodies of water from Indiana to New Mexico, and south to the Gulf and extreme northeast Mexico. They average 12.5–20 cm (5–8 in). In the wild, they are often observed basking on logs jutting from the water, but for many people they are most often observed in pet stores. They are called cooters or sliders in various parts of the country. The distinctive broad reddish stripe behind the eye, from which their name is derived, often darkens with age and is obliterated. Consequently, adult specimens are easily confused with other basking turtles. The chin, neck, and legs are marked by light-colored streaks. The plastron of young turtles is profusely marked by dark eyelike spots. With age, these often disappear and adults may have a plain yellow plastron.

Turtles incubated at cooler temperatures had thinner leg stripes, wider chin stripes, and less plastral pigmentation. Elevated carbon dioxide levels during incubation widened leg and chin stripes and decreased the number of plastral spots.

The implications of these findings are of considerable importance to scientists studying developmental anatomy, evolution, and even taxonomy. For example, the Mississippi map turtle (*Graptemys kohnii*) and the false map turtle (*Graptemys pseudogeographica*), two turtles with large overlapping ranges, are so similar that the best way to tell one from the other is by a head marking. The Mississippi map turtle has a light-colored crescent behind the eye and the false map turtle does not, but head pigmentation has been demonstrated to be very temperature-sensitive in this genus. In egg clutches from both, *kohnii* pattern appeared almost exclusively in eggs incubated at 25°C, and at 30°C only 5 of 165 eggs yielded *kohnii* head patterns.[16]

The general coloration of adult alligators is black, but the young are boldly patterned with light crossbands on a black background color, generally eight stripes on the body and 12 on the tail. Cooler incubation temperatures decrease the number of these white stripes by an average of two.[17]

The significance of these findings cannot be lost on herpetoculturists who are selecting for breeding reptiles and amphibians with anomalous color patterns on the assumption that they can produce pure lines with the desired traits. Some of these traits are not hereditary, and it may take generations of breeding to determine this.

We had this experience with an abnormally striped corn snake that was captured in Louisiana. Multiple breedings, including F_1 crosses and F_1's backcrossed to the parent, spread over many years, and involving almost 100 hatchlings, resulted in all wild types. We were finally convinced that the striping in that particular corn snake was not genetic.

ENDNOTES

1. Klauber, L.M. 1936. The California kingsnake, a case of pattern dimorphism. Herpetologica 1:27.
2. Zweifel, R.G. 1981. Genetics of color pattern polymorphism in the California kingsnake. Journal of Heredity. 72:238–244.
3. Reimer, W.J. 1958. Longitudinal striping as a pattern modification in the snake *Pituophis melanoleucus*. Chicago Acad. Sci. Publ. 165:1–9.
4. Bechtel, E.R., and T. Whitecar. 1983. Genetics of striping in the gopher snake, *Pituophis melanoleucus*. Journal of Herpetology 17:362–370.
5. Bechtel, H.B., and E. Bechtel. 1978. Heredity of pattern mutation in the corn snake, *Elaphe g. guttata*, demonstrated by captive breedings. Copeia 4:719–721.
6. Dyrkacz,S. 1982. Striped pattern morphism in the prairie kingsnake, *Lampropeltis c. calligaster*. Herp Review 13:70–71.
7. Gloyd, H.K. 1935. Some aberrant color patterns in snakes. Papers Mich. Acad. Sci., Arts and Letters 20:661–668.
8. Gloyd, H.K. 1958. Aberrations in the color patterns of some crotalid snakes. Papers Mich. Acad. Sci., Arts and Letters. 10:185–195.
9. Nickerson, M.A., and C.E. Mays. 1968. More aberratons in the color patterns of rattlesnakes. The Wasman Journal of Biology. 26:125–131.
10. Gelback, F.R. 1962. Aberrant western milksnake, *Lampropeltis doliata*, Linnaeus, from New Mexico. Southwestern Naturalist. 7:270–272.
11. Fitch, H.S. 1959. A patternless phase of the copperhead. Herpetologica 15:21–24.
12. Moore, J.A. 1942. An embryological and genetical study of *Rana burnsi* Weed. Genetics 27: 408–416.
13. Ballinger, R.E., and C.O. McKinney. 1968. Occurrence of a patternless morph of *Cnemidophorus*. Herpetologica. 24:264–265.
14. Vinegar, A. 1973. The effects of temperature on growth and development of embryos of the Indian python, *Python molurus* (Reptilia: serpentes: boidae). Copeia. 1973 1:171–173.
15. Etchberger, C.R., M.A. Ewert, J.B. Phillips, and C.E. Nelson. 1993. Environmental and maternal influences on embryonic pigmentation in a turtle (*Trachemys scripta elegans*). J. Zool. Lond. 230:529–539.
16. Ewert, M.A. 1979. The embryo and its egg:development and natural history, pp. 333–413. In: Turtles: perspectives and research. M. Harless and H. Morlock (eds.). John Wiley & Sons, New York.
17. Murray,J.D., D.C. Deeming, and M.W.J. Ferguson. 1990. Size-dependent pigmentation-pattern formation in embryos of *Alligator mississippiensis*: time of initiation of pattern generation mechanism. Proc. R. Soc. London. 239:279–293.

12

Scalelessness, Bicephaly, and Hybrids

```
SCALELESSNESS
```

A hatchling Pacific gopher snake was collected in 1971 near Oakland, California. It had an essentially normal color pattern, but aside from a single row of ventrolateral scales and some facial scales, it was virtually devoid of dorsal body scales. The ventral scutes were present but split longitudinally into two to four sections. The skin had the superficial appearance and texture of a naked, newborn mouse.

The scaleless snake was subjected to studies to determine the importance of reptilian scales in water loss and heat transfer.[1] No differences were observed between the scaleless and a wild-type specimen of comparable age and size. With my interest in cutaneous anomalies, however, I was more struck with the snake itself than with its physiology. I had never seen such a snake, and did not know anyone who had.

I subsequently learned that this was not the first scaleless snake reported. A partially scaleless newborn western aquatic garter snake (*Thamnophis couchii*) had been collected in 1942 at King's Canyon, California, and reported in *Copeia*.[2]

Western aquatic garter snakes are ordinarily reddish with dark blotches and a well-defined yellowish dorsal stripe. Six races of this species range from southern Oregon south into Baja California and east into western Nevada. Coloration varies among the subspecies, and not all races possess the prominent dorsal stripe. They are large garter snakes, averaging 46–144.8 cm (18–57 in). They are named for their preference for rivers and streams, where they can find fish, frogs, toads, and other aquatic prey.

The partially scaleless specimen was light green with shiny black blotches and a darker green dorsal stripe. It lacked all dorsal scales aside from a few head scales, and had normal ventrals.

When I first became aware of the fact that scaleless snakes existed, nothing was known regarding the genetics, and it was not even certain that a mutation was the cause. Even though specimens were so rare that most herpetologists never had seen one, we had two opportunities to investigate the genetics of this anomaly.

Ken Fahey, a herpetologist from Georgia, loaned us a scaleless male mole snake

(*Lampropeltis calligaster rhombomaculata*) that had been collected as a juvenile in Mississippi in 1978. Mole snakes are medium sized and widely distributed from Maryland into Florida and west into Mississippi and Tennessee. They are rarely seen, however, spending much of their time burrowing. They average 76–102 cm (30–40 in). They are ordinarily light to dark brown with distinct dark-edged reddish-brown blotches, but older specimens often lose their markings and become plain brown. In common with other kingsnakes, they eat snakes occasionally, but they also feed on lizards and small mammals.

The scaleless specimen, which is still living, is essentially devoid of all dorsal scales aside from some head scales. The ventrals are divided by a deep cleft extending the length of the snake's body. In addition to lacking scales, it is abnormally colored: creamy white with sooty black blotches.

We were not successful in determining the genetics of scalelessness with this snake. It was bred with a wild type, resulting in three wild-type offspring. These did not survive to sexual maturity, and we were not able to induce any subsequent breedings.

In 1985 we obtained two hatchling scaleless Texas rat snakes, a male and a female, from the Bronx Zoo through the generosity of John Behler, curator of herpetology. The female died of cryptosporidiosis, a gastrointestinal disease caused by a protozoan (a microscopic single-celled organism) of the genus *Cryptosporidia*. In spite of the fact that the organisms are widespread in nature, infections in snakes are rare, which is fortunate, since no satisfactory therapy exists.

The surviving male was virtually devoid of all dorsal scales except some ventrolateral ones and a few head scales, and those scales that were present were attenuated nubbins. The ventrals were divided by a deep cleft the length of the snake's body, creating the appearance of parallel rows of ventrals. When fully grown, he was brick red with smoky blotches.

He was raised to sexual maturity, and we were able to demonstrate that scalelessness in the Texas rat snake is caused by an autosomal recessive gene mutation.[3] In 1987 he was bred to a wild type, resulting in four wild-type young, three females and a male. The three female F_1's were bred back to the original male in 1989, producing clutches of six, seven, and 10 eggs. These 23 eggs produced four male and five female scaleless hatchlings, and 14 wild types. In 1990 F_1's were crossed, producing two clutches containing a total of 22 eggs. All hatched, producing one male and four female scaleless phenotypes, and 17 wild types. All snakes homozygous for the recessive mutation are scaleless, identical to the original male.

During embryogenesis, dorsal scales form by backward overlaps of epidermis and the outermost dermis. This differentiation starts as soon as the embryo is covered by a distinct primordial dermis and epidermis. The normally unpaired ventrals arise as paired structures, fusing at the midline prior to birth or hatching. Features of the scaleless mutation indicate that, by some mechanism, it interrupts completion of the terminal steps of scutellation. While a mutation of this magnitude would be expected to be harmful if not lethal, the scaleless snakes have no functional disabilities resulting from their lack of scales.

I examined an adult scaleless eastern garter snake from Chatham County,

Georgia. A homeowner discovered it in 1989, killed it, and took it to the Savannah Science Museum where it was identified. It was brick red with a yellow dorsal stripe and alternating smoky blotches on the sides. It was similar to the other scaleless snakes in that it lacked dorsal scales, but unlike the mole snake and the Texas rat snake, the ventral scales were normal (undivided). It was noted that the ventrals of the western aquatic garter snake were also normal. The significance of this is not clear.

Scaleless snakes have appeared in experimental breeding situations, which is not surprising, since much captive breeding involves inbreeding, increasing the chance of exposing rare concealed recessive genes. A cross between two albino western diamondback rattlesnakes in a captive breeding situation at the Atlanta Zoo produced two litters that contained young with no dorsal scales and undivided ventrals. Littermates included normal snakes and snakes with other scale anomalies. These snakes were part of the gene pool from an experimental breeding colony of snakes that contained albinism, diverse scale anomalies, and some cranial aberrations.[4] It is probably significant that the wild-caught albino female snake from which this colony originated had scale anomalies. She had notable reduction or absence of scales in the frontal and prefrontal areas of the head, bare skin where the intercanthals should have been, only three intersupraoculars, and two large kidney-shaped scales immediately behind the supraoculars (T. Logan, personal communication, 1976).

The scaleless mole snake and Texas rat snakes in our possession move and feed normally, but they often have difficulty in shedding, since the cast is very thin and does not have the "stretch" present in the skin of snakes with normal scutellation. Consequently, the cast often rolls into a tight band at the thick mid-section of the snake. Scaleless snakes have a normal eye cap.

Regarding incidence, very few wild-caught scaleless snakes have been reported. Since anyone who kills a snake with no scales is likely to notice something different about it and take it somewhere for identification, the lack of reports probably indicates that specimens are rare in nature. This could indicate low mutation rate, low survival of mutated individuals, or both.

BICEPHALY AND SIAMESE TWINS

Two-headed (bicephalic) reptiles make news, and usually get their pictures in the newspaper. Larger two-headed animals were the bread and butter of sideshows. Though bicephalic reptiles and amphibians do not fall within my interest in color pattern, they are naturally occurring variants of a very conspicuous nature, and they certainly prompt many questions: "What causes it?"; "How do they eat?"; "Is it hereditary?"

Bicephalic snakes are the equivalent of Siamese twins in humans, and Siamese twins are identical twins with incomplete separation. Identical twins result when a fertilized egg divides at an early developmental stage, and the two halves go on to produce separate individuals. They are identical since both have the same genotype.

When there is incomplete separation of a fertilized egg, the partially divided egg proceeds to become a body with two heads. The division may even be more extensive, resulting in two nearly complete bodies joined at some point, the abdomen for example, or even the head.

Feeding is a problem for bicephalic snakes, since snakes swallow their prey whole. When both heads are hungry at the same time, care must be taken that both heads do not try to swallow the same animal. Captive specimens can be fed small prey, but even then the snakes must be observed carefully to prevent a food fight between the two heads. I have never heard of an adult wild-caught bicephalic snake. It is unlikely that one could survive, since it would probably starve due to the feeding problem.

Feeding is less of a problem with two-headed turtles. They eat smaller bites, and the two heads are less apt to get into a food fight.

Bicephalic snakes have difficulty in exiting from their eggs. Several years ago we had a clutch of corn snake eggs that all hatched except two. I waited about six days and opened the two that had not hatched, and salvaged two live hatchlings. About a week later, when discarding the hatched eggs, I discovered an unhatched egg that I had overlooked. It contained a dead, fully-developed, two-headed snake that had made multiple slits in the egg, but was unable to emerge.

Regarding the cause of bicephaly, since it is imperfect twinning, there may be a hereditary basis. In humans, at least, the tendency for twinning in some families is known to nearly everybody, and it is logical to infer that the same applies to reptiles and amphibians. A number of toxic, physical, and infectious agents are known to be teratogenic (capable of causing fetal malformations and monstrosities). The general roughing out of the reptile or amphibian body occurs in the early weeks of development, and exposure to a teratogen at this critical stage of embryogenesis is the most likely time to cause bicephaly and other birth defect.

HYBRIDS

When an unusual snake, or any other animal for that matter, is discovered, many people are quick to conclude that it must be a hybrid. Like two-headed animals, hybrids and alleged hybrids are favorite attractions for sideshows and carnivals. "For the price of one ticket, see the only cross between a rabbit and a wolf!" This is sure to get some gawkers. In most cases, the odd animal is a deformed example of some known species, but "crosses" cannot be dismissed out of hand. The barker may be right sometimes. Hybridization can occur, and surely does from time to time.

A hybrid is the offspring of two parents that differ in one or more heritable characters. It may be at the subspecific, specific, or even the generic level, though the genetic differences between animals of different genera make hybridization unlikely.

Hybrid snakes at the subspecific level are called intergrades. They are common where the ranges of subspecies abut. Anyone who has hunted snakes along the Carolina coasts knows about intergrades. Where the black rat snake and yellow rat snake ranges meet, many of the snakes have characteristics common to both, and are difficult to assign to one or the other on the basis of color pattern. Subspecies are genetically very similar to one another.

Interspecific hybridization is less common, but it does happen. Wild-caught snakes with morphologic evidence suggestive of being interspecific hybrids are collected occasionally, but it is difficult to prove. Captive hybridization between species, on the other hand, has been confirmed. As early as 1933 a cross between a female yellow chicken snake and a corn snake was reported by Lederer.[5] The offspring were fertile and later backcrossed with the yellow chicken snake.

My nephew and I successfully mated a male corn snake to a yellow chicken snake in 1958.[6] The patterns and coloration of the 14 hatchlings from this mating differed from both parents, and were intermediate between the two. Two of them had unilateral microophthalmia (small eyes) and one had bilateral microophthalmia. A pair raised to maturity proved to be fertile.

Hybrids between genera are not common because they have too many differing genetically determined characteristics. However, crosses between *Elaphe* × *Lampropeltis* and *Elaphe* × *Pituophis* have been induced in captive breeding situations. Information regarding intergeneric hybridization was furnished to me by Kevin Enge, a herpetologist from Tallahassee, Florida (personal communication, 1994). Though various techniques may be resorted to, the hybridization is effected by tricking a courting male by switching females or placing the male's tail on the wrong female immediately prior to copulation. The offspring from the crosses mentioned inherit some characteristics from each parent and have proved fertile in spite of their wide genetic differences.

Many factors make intergeneric hybridization unlikely, even though the snakes may have overlapping (sympatric) ranges, with obvious opportunity for some physical contact with each other. Constraints of different size prevents some hybridization. Within their ranges, different species occupy different microhabitats, have different habits, and have different breeding seasons and breeding habits. Also, they are attracted by pheromones from their own species. Finally, the paired male hemipenes (male sexual organs) differ in each species. The hemipenes differ not only in size related to the size of the snake, but their surface is arranged in spines and finger-like projections arranged in rosettes called calyces. The arrangement of these calyces is so distinctive for each species that hemipenes can be used as identification characters. It has been speculated that these embellishments hold the hemipenes in place during copulation long enough to insure fertilization, and also that a major purpose may be to prevent hybridization.

ENDNOTES

1. Licht, P., and A.F. Bennett. 1972. A scaleless snake: tests of the role of reptilian scales in water loss and heat transfer. Copeia. 4:702–707.
2. Stickel, W.H. 1942. A partially scaleless garter snake. Copeia. 1942:181.

3. Bechtel, H.B., and E. Bechtel. 1991. Scaleless snakes and a breeding report of scaleless *Elaphe obsoleta lindheimeri*. Herp Rev. 22:12–14.

4. Murphy, J.B., J.E. Rehg, P.F.A. Maderson, and W.B. McCrady. 1987. Scutellation and pigmentation defects in a laboratory colony of western diamondback rattlesnakes (*Crotalus atrox*): mode of inheritance. Herpetologica. 43:292–300.

5. Lederer, V.G. 1950. Ein bastard von *Elaphe guttata* (Linne)- × *Elaphe qu. quadrivittata* (Holbrook)- und dessen ruckkreuzung mit der mutterlichen ausgangstart. Der Zoologische Garten. 17:235–242.

6. Bechtel, H.B., and J. Mountain. 1960. Interspecific hybridization between two snakes of the genus *Elaphe*. Copeia. 2:151–153.

13

Investigative Breeding and Artificial Selection

When I first became interested in herpetology in the 1930's, I began looking for reptiles and amphibians in all of my spare time, and quickly became familiar with most of those found in my home state of Pennsylvania. During one vacation my family visited the Hershey Zoo, which had a small reptile collection. I saw for the first time large pythons and boas, exotic venomous snakes, and other exciting snakes that I knew only from books and pictures. They made the blacksnake racers, garter snakes, and water snakes that I had been finding pale by comparison. I still recall clearly the ball python (*Python regius*), and how I wanted to have one. In the 1930's I may as well have wanted my own Cadillac.

Ball pythons are the smallest of the African true pythons, rarely exceeding 120 cm (48 in). They are thickset and have a bold pattern consisting of large tan or yellow ovoids on a dark brown background. The name is derived from their habit of rolling into a compact ball when threatened, with the head and tail tucked safely out of sight, leaving no loose ends sticking out for predators to grab. The ball is so round that it can be rolled on a flat surface. I have seen a black rat snake and some other snakes roll into a ball under similar circumstances, but they have not perfected it. Ball pythons are native to West Africa, where they frequent mammal burrows for refuge, for incubating their eggs, and also for hunting. They feed on small rodents.

A great number of changes have occurred since World War II, and today a young person with an interest in herpetology faces a different world. Improved communication and transportation have made available in pet stores reptiles and amphibians that were previously seen only in zoos. Meanwhile a human population explosion is destroying and degrading natural habitats at an accelerating pace. Entire animal populations are disappearing, and many reptiles and amphibians have the dubious distinction of being endangered species. Coinciding with these profound changes, captive reptile and amphibian propagation has progressed from a hit-or-miss operation to a mass business, and the herpetoculturists can breed pure lines of unusual specimens. Today, a young person does not have to settle for the conventional garter snake as his first snake. He can as easily have a ball python. While many are still imported from Africa, numbers are being captive bred.

Even though they are native to Africa, ball pythons are among the snakes most readily available in pet stores. I finally acquired one in 1959 and found out that my

99

first instinct about them was correct. They are very satisfying captives. They are hardy and thrive for years in captivity if provided with a spacious cage, a hiding box, drinking water, and an ample supply of small rodents. They are docile and rarely bite, but they lose the instinct to roll up into a ball after adjusting to captivity. Thirty-four years later, mine is still alive.

As more ball pythons are captured and bred, mutant genes are being uncovered. Pure lines of albinos and axanthic specimens have been bred, and piebald specimens are known.

THE GREEN BURMESE PYTHON

The Burmese python is another former zoo snake that has become a popular pet store item. These snakes have an attractive pattern, a generally docile disposition, and a gratifying size. For some reason, many people, as soon as they get interested in acquiring a snake, want either a large snake or a poisonous snake. In most cases, someone in the household has enough common sense to veto the poisonous variety, so the big one wins out. Big snakes have big appetites, require big cages, and make big messes, but this does not stop the traffic. That said, for those with a legitimate reason for owning one, Burmese pythons are nice animals. Pure albino and other mutant strains have been developed.

Tom Weidner acquired an immature male patternless light green Burmese python in 1974. On his way home to Iowa from a collecting trip in Florida, he stopped to visit us and showed me a picture of the snake. He wanted to breed the snake and asked me if I thought it would be heritable. I told him that I did not know, but that he could find out if he would be patient enough to breed a few generations of pythons. He was and he did.

The snake mated with a wild type sometime during the fall and winter of 1981–1982 (personal communication, 1993). The mating resulted in 18 eggs, all of which hatched into wild types. The male died before any of the F_1 daughters could be bred back to him, but an F_1 cross in 1985 produced green offspring in numbers consistent with an autosomal recessive mutation. The newly hatched mutants were rich greenish-brown with variable dark dorsal markings. Tom stopped at our house in 1985, on the way to Florida, to show us these interesting and attractive little snakes. Subsequently, pure lines have been bred by Tom and others, and they are called green Burmese pythons. Unfortunately, they become somewhat drab with age.

THE BRINDLE BLACK RAT SNAKE

The gray rat snake (*Elaphe o. spiloides*) is a common harmless snake of the southeast from southwest Georgia west to Mississippi and north in the Mississippi Valley to southern Illinois and Indiana. Gray rat snakes are large constricting snakes, averaging 106.7–183 cm (42–72 in), and variable in color. Some are silvery-gray with dark blotches, while others are darker and the blotches brownish, but the blotches always stand out from the background color. In south Georgia they are commonly called chicken snakes because of their penchant for hen houses. A large adult can easily swallow a chicken egg. Eggs are swallowed whole and, after the egg is well into the gut, the snake breaks the egg by pushing the area where the egg is up against the side of the cage. Aside from the occasional nuisance snake in the hen house, most of them feed on small mammals and birds. They are also called oak snakes because of their association with hardwood forests. Gray rat snakes are good climbers, and often are found searching for food in trees and up in rafters. They are still common in the built-up areas of Valdosta and are constantly getting into homes. A snake in the house is usually a gray rat snake.

The gray rat snake, black rat snake, and yellow rat snake are very closely related, all belonging to the genus *Elaphe*. The black rat snake ranges from southern Canada south into Georgia, and the yellow rat snake ranges from Florida north into Georgia. The hatchlings of all three are gray with brownish or darker gray blotches. As they mature, black rat snakes become uniform black, yellow rat snakes become yellow with longitudinal black stripes, and gray rat snakes retain their juvenile color and pattern. Where their ranges abut in middle Georgia they interbreed, and intergrade specimens with characteristics of any or all three are common. It is often impossible to assign a specimen to any one of the subspecies.

A male rat snake (*obsoleta*) was collected in 1974 near Macon, Georgia, in the area of intergradation for these rat snakes. It could not be identified as one of the recognized subspecies, and it did not possess characteristics normally associated with an intergrade. It was essentially tan with reddish brown blotches, prominent white flecks at some of the scale edges, and no clear-cut pattern. The pupils were black and the tongue red. For identification purposes, we designated it as brindle.

We obtained the snake on a breeding loan from the Savannah Science Museum, and were successful in demonstrating that its color pattern anomaly was caused by an autosomal recessive gene mutation.[1] The first breeding in 1977, with a wild-type black rat snake, resulted in seven wild-type hatchlings. Three were retained for future breeding. F_1 crosses in 1980 resulted in eight wild types. A cross in 1981 between the original male and an F_1 daughter resulted in eight wild types and one brindle. An F_1 cross in 1983 resulted in eight wild types and one brindle. Subsequent matings produced ratios between brindles and wild types consistent with the classical Mendelian ratios seen with recessive mutations.

We bred the brindle to a tyrosinase-positive albino black rat snake to learn if the brindle mutation could possibly be caused by another recessive allele at the albino locus. The mating resulted in nine eggs, and all hatched as wild types. Though somewhat hypomelanistic, the brindle rat snake is not an albino.

THE GOLDEN YELLOW CALIFORNIA KINGSNAKE

Artificial selection has been used for years to accentuate and perpetuate desired inherited traits in birds and animals. Mice have been inbred for color, susceptibility to cancer, hairlessness, and other characteristics that make them valuable for research. Cattle have been inbred for higher butterfat yield. Any person who purchases a common goldfish is looking at the end result of centuries of selective breeding involving the Chinese carp, a common fish in sluggish waters throughout China. It is characteristically a nondescript brownish green, but more than three centuries ago, fish culturists noted that some of them possessed an unusual amount of gold pigment in the scales. They inbred these over many generations, selecting the ones with the most gold for each breeding, and succeeded in producing a gold fish. Further generations of inbreeding uncovered other recessive genes controlling color, plus rare genes controlling fin morphology, body form, and eye shape. Pure lines with desired characteristics have been produced, some quite bizarre: plump black bodies, fan tails, pop eyes, and other features never seen in a wild type. Nevertheless they are still carp. When goldfish are released back into the wild, through natural selection they revert to the green brown wild type after a few generations.

Present day husbandry techniques make selective breeding possible with reptiles and amphibians; the creation of pure albino strains, for example. Creation of albino strains is the simplest form of selective breeding, since albinism is controlled by a single recessive gene. The only difficulty in breeding a pure line of albinos is finding the first one.

Once the parameters for husbandry of any species have been established, it is possible to select for other traits. When a trait is controlled by multiple alleles, it can be accentuated by selective breeding. Steve Osborne, a herpetologist from Murrieta, California, provided me with a striking slide of a California kingsnake that is almost entirely yellow, along with a description of the breeding involved in producing the snake (personal communication, 1993).

California kingsnakes are typically black or brown with yellow or white markings, falling into two standard patterns: ringed or striped. However, they are very polymorphic. There is great individual variation in the quality, quantity, and proportions of both colors, and these variations are under genetic control.

The golden yellow strain originated from wild-caught snakes, and selecting for initial breeding stock those with the greatest amount of yellow in their pattern. With each successive generation, those with the most yellow were selected for inbreeding, and it was apparent that those with the most yellow produced young with the most yellow, or even more yellow than any preceding generation. Within approximately 12 generations, starting in the 1960's, a snake with the dorsal surface approximately 95% yellow has been produced. Raising 12 generations of baby snakes is a tremendous effort, and several other persons were involved at one time or another.

DIHYBRID VARIANTS

Captive breeding of reptiles and amphibians, especially snakes, has completely altered the incidence of variants. Reptiles and amphibians have become popular pets, and stores are carrying them in addition to the usual stock of puppies, kittens, fish, and birds.

Snakes that breed readily in captivity are being produced by the thousands to satisfy this demand, and much of the demand is for exotic and atypical specimens. In an effort to satisfy customers that are increasingly eclectic, pure lines of albinos and other uncommon mutants are being bred in species after species. Intense collecting worldwide, with emphasis on searching for anomalous snakes by collectors, is funnelling variants into the hands of herpetoculturists, who can now breed even the difficult species. They are using knowledge of genetics to produce pure lines with unusual colors and patterns, and have taken advantage of knowledge of snake reproductive biology to induce several breedings in one year. There is considerable inbreeding in all of this activity, and new recessive traits are coming to light among these thousands of baby snakes.

Herpetoculturists have taken the process a step further by essentially creating new snakes. In cases where the mutated genes are not linked, they are breeding more than one desired mutation into an individual snake. The most widely known example of this experimentation is the snow corn, simultaneously homozygous for albinism and axanthism. The phenotype is usually creamy yellow with tan blotches, but there is variation. Since it must be assumed that the snow corn has no functional melanophores or xanthophores, the variation in the phenotypes is somewhat surprising.

Other oddities that have been produced are albino striped gopher snakes, albino green Burmese pythons, and striped snow corns. Production of inter-generic hybrids has been discussed in Chapter 12. In truth, whatever some people may make of this controversial practice, many of these bizarre creations are exceptionally beautiful.

While these man-made snakes do not fall in the category of naturally occurring variants, in a way they are, because the mutant genes that make it all possible have occurred naturally. Each of these captive-created variants could have occurred in nature, though the odds against this are infinitely greater than the odds against winning a state lottery.

ENDNOTE

1. Bechtel, H.B., and E. Bechtel. 1985. Genetics of color mutations in the snake, *Elaphe obsoleta*. Journal of Heredity. 76:7–11.

Parting Words

In 1960 we were in Washington, D.C. visiting Lear and Marge Grimmer, friends that I had met on field trips before Bette and I were married. Lear took us on a tour of the National Zoo, where he was assistant administrator. In the reptile house, he took us into the holding area behind the exhibits, an area most zoo visitors know only by the KEEP OUT sign. All of the numerous reptiles and amphibians that are off exhibit are kept behind those doors. Some are newly acquired and still in quarantine, some have health problems, and many surplus specimens are housed there. This area is also where eggs are incubated and young specimens are maintained, and it is a commissary for the unbelievable variety of food items that a large collection of reptiles and amphibians requires.

At that time the zoo was exhibiting a large albino black rat snake, and Lear removed it from its cage for me to get a better look. As I was admiring it, Lear, without any preliminary discussion, handed the snake to me and said, "Here, Bern, take it home with you. It's yours." This was before the era of captive propagation, when albino snakes were still rare, and having one was out of the question for most private individuals. I thought Lear was kidding, but he wasn't. "No," he said, "I'm serious. Freaks don't belong in zoo exhibits."

The snake proved to be a male tyrosinase-negative albino. He lived for many years. We utilized him in a number of different investigative breeding projects, and we learned a lot of what we know about albinism in snakes from him and his progeny. I am confident that many of his descendants are living in cages all over the world, since he was one of the earliest black rat snakes that was used to start a pure albino line.

In succeeding years I have seen many albino snakes of numerous species, more than I thought existed. They are attractive by almost any standard, but at least to me, they are even more fascinating for the miracle that they represent. After all of these years, when I look at one of my black rat snakes that I know is heterozygous for albinism, I still marvel. Hidden within its body, amid thousands of genes, the snake carries just one mutant gene, a particle too tiny to be visible even with an electron microscope, that can transform a black snake with black tongue and black eyes into a peach colored snake with pink blotches, pink tongue, and red eyes.

From time to time, I am reminded of Lear's comment, and he was correct. By definition, albino snakes are freaks, which means that this book is about freaks. True, they are not grotesque monstrosities, as the word generally connotes, but they certainly are not what nature intended them to be. At this time, however, so many albinos and other anomalous color patterns are available, and they are so inherently interesting, that many young people are attracted to them before they give themselves a chance to appreciate the natural beauty of wild-type reptiles and amphibians.

I was fortunate. I learned how fascinating snakes are as found in their natural environment, before I saw an albino, literally before I knew any existed. While I cannot deny that I think most of them are pretty, I look on albinos as snakes with something missing, and certainly not necessarily more beautiful than their wild-type counterparts. If I were allowed just one black rat snake as a cage specimen for my own satisfaction, it would be black, just like the first one I found after getting interested in herpetology. It was my first large snake, and was sunning itself on a rock pile at the edge of a deserted field on the Laurel Ridge in Somerset County, Pennsylvania when I came upon it. If I found the same snake today, instead of 60 years ago, I would wish him well and caution him to be more careful, because the next person might harm or capture him.

Bibliography

GENERAL WORKS

Audesirk, G., and T. Audesirk. 1989. Biology: Life on Earth (second edition). Macmillan Publishing Co., New York.

Ashton, R.E., and P.S. Ashton. 1981. Handbook of Reptiles and Amphibians of Florida: Part One, The Snakes. Windward Publishing, Inc., Miami.

Ashton, R.E., and P.S. Ashton. 1985. Handbook of Reptiles and Amphibians of Florida: Part Two, Lizards, Turtles, and Crocodilians. Windward Publishing, Inc., Miami.

Ashton, R.E., and P.S. Ashton. 1988. Handbook of Reptiles and Amphibians of Florida: Part Three, The Amphibians. Windward Publishing, Inc., Miami.

Behler, J.L., and F.W. King. 1979. The Audubon Society Field Guide to North American Reptiles and Amphibians. Alfred A. Knopf, New York.

Bellairs, A.d'A. 1970. The Life of Reptiles, Volume 2. Universe Books, New York.

Cochran, D.M. 1961. Living Amphibians of the World. Doubleday & Company Inc. Garden City, NY.

Cogger, H.C. 1975. Reptiles and Amphibians of Australia. A.H. & A.W. Reed, Sidney.

Conant, R., and J.T. Collins. 1991. Reptiles and Amphibians of Eastern/Central North America. Houghton Mifflin Co., Boston.

Duellman, W.E., and L. Trueb. 1986. Biology of Amphibians. McGraw-Hill Book Co., New York.

Halliday, T., and K. Adler. (eds). 1986. The Encyclopedia of Reptiles and Amphibians. Facts on File Inc., New York.

Klauber, L.M. 1972. Rattlesnakes, Their Habits, Life Histories, and Influence on Mankind. 2 vols. Univ. of California Press, Berkeley.

Mehrtens, J.M. 1987. Living Snakes of the World, in Color. Sterling Publishing Co., Inc., New York.

Minton, S.A. Jr., and M.R. Minton. 1973. Giant Reptiles. Charles Scribner's Sons, New York.

Minton, S.A. Jr., and M.R. Minton. 1980. Venomous Reptiles, Revised Edition. Charles Scribner's Sons, New York.

Noble, G.K. 1931. The Biology of the Amphibia. Dover Publications, Inc., New York.

Porter, K.R. 1972. Herpetology. W.B. Saunders Co., Philadelphia.

Pritchard, P.C.H. 1979. Encyclopedia of Turtles. T.F.H. Publications, Jersey City, NJ.

Schmidt, K.P., and R.F. Inger. 1957. Living Reptiles of the World. Hanover House, Garden City, NY.

Shaw, C.E., and S. Campbell. 1974. Snakes of the American West. Alfred A. Knopf, New York.

Stebbins, R.C. 1966. A Field Guide to Western Reptiles and Amphibians. Houghton Mifflin Co., Boston.

Wright, A.H., and A.A. Wright. 1957. Handbook of Snakes of the United States and Canada. Comstock Publ. Assoc. Ithica, NY.

Zug, G.R. 1993. Herpetology, An Introductory Biology of Amphibians and Reptiles. Academic Press, Inc., San Diego.

CHROMATOPHORE BIOLOGY

Bagnara, J. 1983. Developmental aspects of vertebrate chromatophores. Amer. Zool. 23:465–478.

Quevedo, W.C.Jr, T.B. Fitzpatrick, G. Szabo, and K. Jimbo. 1987. Biology of Melanocytes in Dermatology in General Medicine, 3rd edition, edited by T.B. Fitzpatrick et al. McGraw-Hill, New York: pp. 225–251.

Taylor, J.D., and J.T. Bagnara. 1972. Dermal Chromatophores. American Zoologist. 12:43–62.

Wick, M.M., V.J. Hearing, and H. Rorsman. 1987. Biochemistry of Melanization in Dermatology in General Medicine, 3rd edition, edited by T.B. Fitzpatrick et al. McGraw-Hill, New York: pp. 251–258.

Witkop, C.J. Jr. 1971. Albinism. Advances in Human Genetics. Vol. 2. Plenum Publ., New York.

COLOR SECTION

Snakes

Dumeril's Boa
Acrantophis dumerili

Normal and Pattern Anomaly
Photo by Gary Lorio

Copperhead
Agkistrodon contortrix (ssp.)

A.

B.

C.

A. Normal
   Photo by H. B. Bechtel
B. Pattern Anomaly
   Photo by Michael W. Hammock
C. Albino
   Photo by Bill Christie
D. Melanistic
   Photo by Alvin Braswell
E. Patternless
   Photo by Bill Love/Glades Herp Inc.
F. Striped Pattern Anomaly
   Photo by Bill Love/Glades Herp Inc.

D.

E.

F.

113

Cottonmouth
Agkistrodon piscivorus (ssp.)

A. Normal
   Photo by H. B. Bechtel
B. Leucistic
   Photo by Bill Love/Glades Herp Inc.
C. Pattern Anomaly
   Photo by Jaime Villa

A.

B.

C.

Boa
Boa constrictor (ssp.)

A.

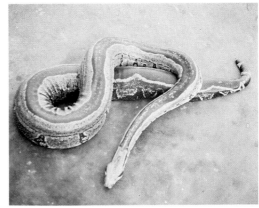

B.

A. Normal
   Photo by H. B. Bechtel
B. Striped Pattern Anomaly
   Photo by Bill Love/
   Glades Herp Inc.
C. Albino
   Photo by H. B. Bechtel
D. Axanthic
   Photo by H. B. Bechtel

C.

D.

Scarlet Snake
Cemophora coccinea

A. Normal
   Photo by H. B. Bechtel
B. Albino
   Photo by James Stuart
C. Striped Pattern Anomaly
   Photo by Glen N. Johnson

A.

B.

C.

Green Tree Python
Chondropython viridis

A.

A. Normal
*Photo by Bill Love/
Glades Herp Inc.*
B. Green and Blue Phase
*Photo by Trooper Walsh
Courtesy of National
Zoological Park*

B.

Northern Black Racer
Coluber constrictor

A. Normal
   Photo by H. B. Bechtel
B. Albino, Juvenile
   Photo by H. B. Bechtel

A.

B.

Northwestern Neotropical Rattlesnake
Crotalus durissus culminatus

Albino and Normal
Photo by Manny Rubio

Eastern Diamondback Rattlesnake
Crotalus adamanteus

A.

B.

A. Normal
   Photo by Richard S. Funk
B. Leucistic
   Photo by Bill Love/
   Glades Herp Inc.
C. Hypomelanistic
   Photo by Mark Pellicer
D. Albino
   Photo by H. B. Bechtel
E. Patternless
   Photo by Andrew Koukoulis
F. Axanthic
   Photo by Robert Simons
G. Striped Pattern Anomaly
   Photo by Dick Flood

C.

D.

E.

F.

G.

121

Western Diamondback Rattlesnake
Crotalus atrox

A. Patternless
   Photo by Manny Rubio
B. Normal
   Photo by H. B. Bechtel
C. Melanistic
   Photo by Craig McIntyre
D. Scaleless Albino
   Photo by Greg Greer
E. Albino
   Photo by Manny Rubio

A.

B.

C.

D.

E.

Timber Rattlesnake
Crotalus horridus

A. Normal
   Photo by William H. Smith
B. Striped Pattern Anomaly
   Photo by Gerard Salmon
C. Hypomelanistic
   Photo by Ted Kahn

A.

B.

C.

Pacific Rattlesnake
Crotalus viridis helleri

A. Normal
   Photo by Ron Everhart
B. Albino
   Photo by Manny Rubio
C. Gray Phase
   Photo by Manny Rubio

A.

B.

C.

Yellow-Faced Whipsnake
Desmansia psammophis

A.

A. Albino
*Photo courtesy of
Queensland Museum
Brisbane, Australia*
B. Normal
Photo by Sherman A. Minton

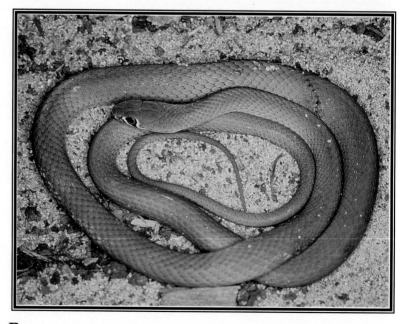

B.

Japanese Rat Snake
Elaphe climacophora

A.

A. Normal
   Photo By Patrick Briggs
   Courtesy of Lloyd Lemke
B. Albino
   Photo by H. B. Bechtel

B.

Mexican Rat Snake
Elaphe flavirufa pardalina

A.

A. Axanthic
   Photo by Terry Vandeventer
B. Normal
   Photo by Terry Vandeventer

B.

Great Plains Rat Snake
Elaphe guttata emoryi

A.

A. Normal
   Photo by Sherman A. Minton
B. Striped Pattern Anomaly
   Photo by Bill Love/Glades Herp Inc.

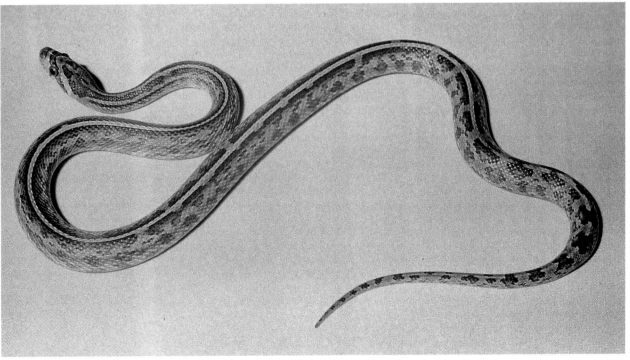

B.

Corn Snake
Elaphe g. guttata

A.

B.

A. Striped Pattern Anomaly
   Photo by H. B. Bechtel
B. Snow Corn
   Photo by Richard S. Funk
C. Striped Pattern Anomaly
   Photo by H. B. Bechtel
D. Normal with Albino
   Photo by H. B. Bechtel
E. Normal with Axanthic
   Photo by H. B. Bechtel
F. Piebald
   Photo by Bill Girden
G. Two-headed
   Photo by Bill Love/
   Glades Herp Inc.
H. Zigzag Pattern Anomaly
   Photo by Bill Love/
   Glades Herp Inc.

C.

D.

E.

F.

G.

H.

131

Texas Rat Snake
Elaphe obsoleta lindheimeri

A.

B.

C.

D.

A. Leucistic
    Photo by H. B. Bechtel
B. Color Pattern
    Anomaly
    Photo by Paul Freed
C. Two-headed
    *Photo by Bill Love/
    Glades Herp Inc.*
D. Normal with Scaleless
    Photo by H. B. Bechtel
E. Normal with Axanthic
    Photo by H. B. Bechtel

E.

Yellow Rat Snake
Elaphe obsoleta quadrivittata

A. Axanthic
   Photo by Richard Bartlett
B. Normal
   Photo by H. B. Bechtel
C. Color Pattern Anomaly
   Photo by Richard Bartlett

A.

B.

C.

Black Rat Snake
Elaphe o. obsoleta

A

B.

C.

A. Normal
   Photo by H. B. Bechtel
B. Albino
   Photo by Richard S. Funk
C. Brindle Mutation
   Photo by Richard S. Funk
D. Striped Pattern Anomaly, Juvenile
   Photo by Alvin Braswell
E. Xanthic Albino
   Photo by H. B. Bechtel
F. Hypomelanistic
   Photo by H. B. Bechtel

134

D.

E.

F.

Gray Rat Snake
Elaphe obsoleta spiloides

Normal with Albino
Photo by Kevin Enge

A.

Mud Snake
Farancia a. abacura

B.

C.

A. Normal
   Photo by H. B. Bechtel
B. Axanthic
   Photo by Bill Love/Glades Herp Inc.
C. Albino
   Photo by H. B. Bechtel

137

Eastern Hognose Snake
Heterodon platyrhinos

A.

B.

C.

D.

A. Color Anomaly
   Photo by H. B. Bechtel
B. Normal (Black Phase)
   Photo by H. B. Bechtel
C. Albino
   Photo by H. B. Bechtel
D. Normal (Patterned Phase)
   Photo by H. B. Bechtel

Prairie Kingsnake
Lampropeltis c. calligaster

A. Normal
   Photo by H. B. Bechtel
B. Striped Pattern Anomaly
   Photo by Mark D. Worthey
C. Albino
   Photo by H. B. Bechtel
D. Striped Pattern Anomaly
   Photo by H. B. Bechtel

A.

B.

C.

D.

Mole Kingsnake
Lampropeltis calligaster rhombomaculata

A. Normal
   Photo by H. B. Bechtel
B. Scaleless
   Photo by H. B. Bechtel

A.

B.

California Kingsnake
Lampropeltis getula californiae

A. Exaggerated yellow by selective breeding
   Photo by John Walling
   Courtesy of Steve Osborne
B. Normal (striped phase)
   Photo by H. B. Bechtel
C. Normal (banded phase)
   Photo by H. B. Bechtel
D. Albino
   Photo by H. B. Bechtel
E. Exaggerated white by selective breeding
   Photo by John Walling
   Courtesy of Steve Osborne

A.

B.

C.

D.

E.

Florida Kingsnake
Lampropeltis getula floridana

A. Normal
  Photo by H. B. Bechtel
B. Hypomelanistic
  Photo by Bill Love/Glades Herp Inc.
C. Axanthic
  Photo by Kevin Enge

A.

B.

C.

Eastern Chain Kingsnake
Lampropeltis g. getula

A. Normal
   Photo by H. B. Bechtel
B. Striped Pattern Anomaly
   Photo by Kevin Enge

A.

B.

Speckled Kingsnake
Lampropeltis getula holbrooki

A. Normal
   Photo by H. B. Bechtel
B. Color Pattern Anomaly
   Photo by Robert A. Young

A.

B.

Sonoran Kingsnake
Lampropeltis getula splendida

Normal with Albino
Photo by Bill Love/Glades Herp Inc.

Queretaro Kingsnake
Lampropeltis ruthveni

A.

A. Albino
   Photo by John Walling
   Courtesy of Steve Osborne
B. Normal
   Photo by Bill Love/Glades Herp Inc.

B.

Scarlet Kingsnake
Lampropeltis triangulum elapsoides

A. Normal
Photo by H. B. Bechtel
B. Albino
Photo by Kevin Enge

A.

B.

Honduran Milk Snake
Lampropeltis triangulum hondurensis

A.

A. Axanthic
   Photo by Daniel P. Johnson
B. Normal
   Photo by H. B. Bechtel

B.

Milk Snake
Lampropeltis t. triangulum

A. Normal (Red Phase)
   Photo by Ted Kahn
B. Color Pattern Anomaly
   Photo by Ted Kahn
C. Albino
   Photo by Ted Kahn
D. Normal
   Photo by H. B. Bechtel

A.

B.

C.

D.

Banded Water Snake
Nerodia f. fasciata

A. Normal
   Photo by H. B. Bechtel
B. Melanistic
   Photo by Dale Cronwell

A.

B.

Northern Water Snake
Nerodia s. sipedon

A.

B.

C.

D.

A. Scaleless
   Photo by James Gerholdt
   Courtesy of Eric Thiss
B. Normal
   Photo by H. B. Bechtel
C. Albino
   Photo by James Gerholdt
   Courtesy of Eric Thiss
D. Color Anomaly
   Photo by James Gerholdt
   Courtesy of Eric Thiss

153

Pacific Gopher Snake
Pituophis melanoleucus catenifer

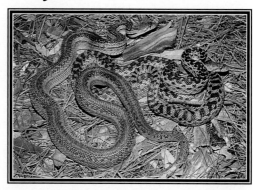

A. Normal and Striped Phase
   Photo by Terry Whitecar
B. Striped Phase
   Photo by H. B. Bechtel
C. Albino
   Photo by Richard Bartlett

A.

B.

C.

154

Northern Pine Snake
Pituophis m. melanoleucus

A.

B.

A. Albino
Photo by Richard Bartlett
B. Normal
Photo by H. B. Bechtel

155

Bull Snake
Pituophis melanoleucus sayi

A.

B.

C.

A. Color Pattern Anomaly
   Photo by Richard Bartlett
B. Albino
   Photo by Richard Bartlett
C. Normal
   Photo by H. B. Bechtel

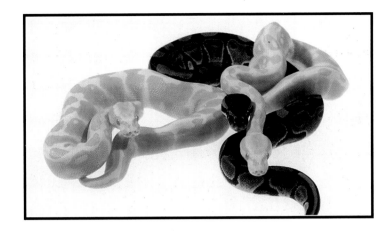

A.

Ball Python
Python regius

A. Normal with Albino
   Photo by Bob Clark
B. Xanthic
   Photo by Greg Greer
C. Striped Pattern Anomaly
   Photo by Greg Greer
D. Piebald
   Photo by Greg Greer

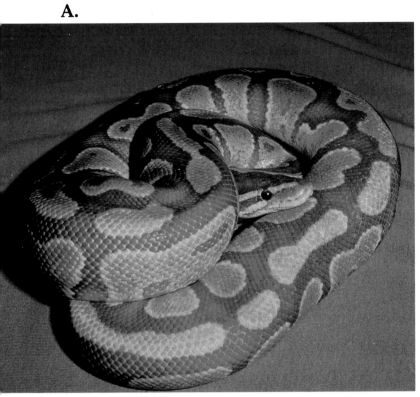

B.

C.

D.

157

Burmese Python
Python molurus bivittatus

A.

B.

C.

D.

E.

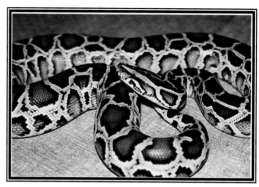

F.

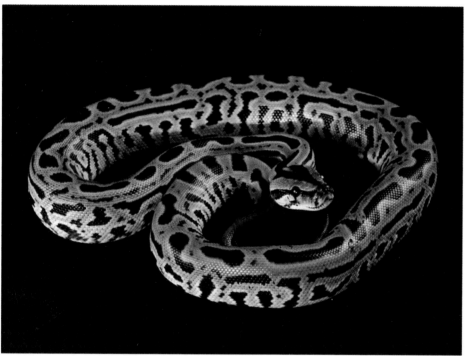

G.

H.

A. Axanthic
   Photo by Terry Vandeventer
B. Calico Color Pattern Anomaly
   Photo by David G. Barker
C. Albino
   Photo by Bill Love/Glades Herp Inc.
D. Green Mutation
   Photo by Tom Weidner
E. Normal with Piebald
   Photo by Tom Weidner
F. Normal
   Photo by H. B. Bechtel
G. Labyrinth Pattern Anomaly
   Photo by Mark Bell
H. Leucistic
   Photo by Bob Clark

159

Reticulated Python
Python reticulatus

A.

A. Normal
   Photo by Al Baldogo
B. Albino
   Photo by Al Baldogo
   Courtesy of Bob Clark
C. Color Pattern Anomaly
   Photo by Al Baldogo

B.

C.

Pine Woods Snake
Rhadinaea flavilata

A.

B.

A. Albino
   Photo by James Gerholdt
B. Normal
   Photo by H. B. Bechtel

Long-Nosed Snake
Rhinocheilus lecontei (ssp.)

A. Normal
   Photo by H. B. Bechtel
B. Striped Pattern Anomaly
   Photo by Bill Love/
   Glades Herp Inc.

A.

B.

Eastern Massasauga
Sistrurus c. catenatus

A. Normal
   Photo by H. B. Bechtel
B. Striped Pattern Anomaly
   Photo by Michael Oldham
C. Melanistic
   Photo by Michael J. Lodato

A.

B.

C.

163

Eastern Garter Snake
Thamnophis s. sirtalis

A.

B.

C.

A. Normal
   Photo by H. B. Bechtel
B. Color Anomaly
   Photo by Ted Kahn
C. Calico Color Pattern Anomaly
   Photo by Richard S. Funk
D. Scaleless
   Photo by H. B. Bechtel
E. Albino
   Photo by Greg Greer
F. Melanistic
   Photo by Kenneth S. Mierzwa

D.

E.

F.

Other Reptiles
and Amphibians

American Alligator
Alligator mississippiensis

A. Normal
   Photo by H. B. Bechtel
B. Normal with Leucistic
   Photo by Curt Burnett
   Courtesy of the Audubon Park Zoo
C. Albino
   Photo by Curt Burnett
   Courtesy of the Audubon Park Zoo
D. Piebald
   Photo by Colleen McDonough

A.

B.

C.

D.

Jefferson Salamander
Ambystoma jeffersonianum

A. Normal
   Photo by H. B. Bechtel
B. Albino
   Photo by Tom Tyning

A.

B.

Spotted Salamander
Ambystoma maculatum

A.

B.

A. Melanistic
   Photo by Ted Kahn
B. Normal
   Photo by H. B. Bechtel

Axolotl
Ambystoma mexicanum

A.

A. Normal, Albino, Leucistic
Photo Courtesy of Indiana University Axolotl Colony
B. Normal and Assorted Color Anomalies
Photo Courtesy of Indiana University Axolotl Colony

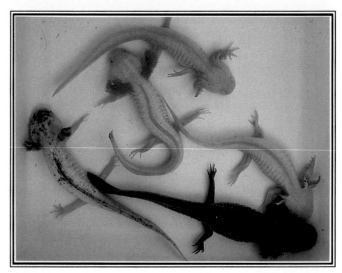

B.

Tiger Salamander
Ambystoma t. tigrinum

A. Normal
   Photo by H. B. Bechtel
B. Albino
   Photo by Jeffrey Black

A.

B.

173

Green Anole
Anolis carolinensis

A.

A. Albino
   Photo by James H. Carmichael
B. Normal
   Photo by H. B. Bechtel

B.

Fowler's Toad
Bufo woodhousii fowleri

A. Normal
   Photo by H. B. Bechtel
B. Axanthic
   Photo by Alvin Braswell

A.

B.

Toad
Bufo (sp.)

A. Normal
   Photo by H. B. Bechtel
B. Albino
   Photo by Greg Greer

A.

B.

Horned Frog
Ceratophrys calcarata

A. Normal
   Photo by Sherman A. Minton
B. Albino
   Photo by H. B. Bechtel

A.

B.

177

Snapping Turtle
Chelydra serpentina

A.

A. Albino
   Photo by Ted Kahn
B. Normal
   Photo by H. B. Bechtel

B.

178

Desert Banded Gecko
Coleonyx v. variegatus

A. Normal
   Photo by Sherman A. Minton
B. Albino
   Photo by Peter J. Mayne

A.

B.

Hellbender
Cryptobranchus alleganiensis (ssp.)

A. Normal
   Photo by H. B. Bechtel
B. Albino
   Photo by Karl Barke

A.

B.

Dusky Salamander
Desmognathus f. fuscus

A.

B.

A. Albino
   Photo by Tom Tyning
B. Normal
   Photo by H. B. Bechtel

Leopard Gecko
Eublepharus macularius

A. Normal and Pattern Anomaly,
   Juvenile
   Photo by H. B. Bechtel
B. Hypomelanistic
   Photo by Pat Murphy

A.

B.

Narrowmouth Toad
Gastrophryne carolinensis

A.

B.

A. Albino
   Photo by Terry Vandeventer
B. Normal
   Photo by H. B. Bechtel

Mississippi Map Turtle
Graptemys kohnii

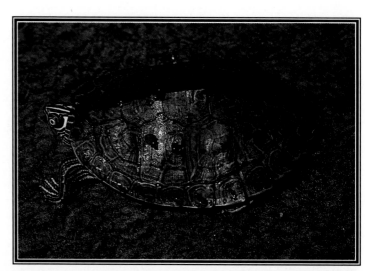

A. Normal
   Photo by Bill Love/Glades Herp Inc.
B. Albino
   Photo by Bill Love/Glades Herp Inc.

A.

B.

Gray Treefrog
Hyla versicolor

A. Brown Phase
   Photo by Ted Kahn
B. Normal
   Photo by H. B. Bechtel
C. Patternless
   Photo by Alvin Braswell

A.

B.

C.

Alligator Snapping Turtle
Macroclemys temminckii

A.

A. Albino
  Photo by Andrew Koukoulis
B. Normal
  Photo by Sherman A. Minton

B.

Northern Velvet Gecko
Oedura castelnaui

A. Normal
   Photo by Richard S. Funk
B. Albino
   Photo by Richard S. Funk

A.

B.

Eastern Glass Lizard
Ophisaurus ventralis

A.

A. Albino
   Photo by Jim Tuten
B. Normal
   Photo by H. B. Bechtel

B.

Asian Water Dragon
Physignathus cocincinus

Normal with Albino
Photo by Jeff Wines

Redback Salamander
Plethodon cinereus

A.

B.

C.

D.

A. Albino
   Photo by Tom Tyning
B. Normal
   Photo by H. B. Bechtel
C. Hypomelanistic
   Photo by Carl D. Anthony
D. Color Anomaly
   Photo by Ted Kahn

Cooter
Pseudemys (sp.)

A. Normal
   Photo by Bill Love/Glades Herp Inc.
B. Two-headed
   Photo by Bill Love/Glades Herp Inc.
C. Albino
   Photo by Bill Love/Glades Herp Inc.

A.

B.

C.

Bullfrog
Rana catesbeiana

A.

B.

A. Normal
   Photo by H. B. Bechtel
B. Albino
   *Photo by Bill Love/
   Glades Herp Inc.*
C. Axanthic
   Photo by Jeff Wines
D. Normal with Axanthic
   Photo by Bill Christie

C.

D.

Leopard Frogs
Northern
Rana pipiens,
Southern
Rana utricularia

A.

A. Hypomelanistic, Southern
   Photo by Richard S. Funk
B. Normal, Northern
   Photo by H. B. Bechtel
C. Burnsi mutant, Northern
   Photo by H. B. Bechtel
D. Burnsi Mutant, Northern
   Photo by Richard S. Funk
E. Albino, Northern
   Photo by Richard S. Funk

C.

D.

E.

Common Musk Turtle
Sternotherus odoratus

A. Normal
   Photo by H. B. Bechtel
B. Albino
   Photo by H. B. Bechtel

A.

B.

Ornate Box Turtle
Terrapene ornata

B.

A. Albino
   *Photo by Bill Love/
   Glades Herp Inc.*
B. Normal
   *Photo by Bill Love/
   Glades Herp Inc.*

Red-Eared Slider
Trachemys scripta elegans

A. Normal
   Photo by Bill Love/Glades Herp Inc.
B. Siamese Twins
   Photo by Larry Collier
C. Albino
   Photo by H. B. Bechtel

A.

B.

C.

196

Clawed Frog
Xenopus laevis

Normal with Albino
Photo by H. B. Bechtel

Desert Gopher Tortoise
Gopherus agassizii*

A. Normal
   Photo by Bill Love/Glades Herp Inc.
B. Albino
   Photo by Bill Love/Glades Herp Inc.

A.

B.

* Reassigned to genus Xerobates

198

Hybrids

A.

B.

A. Intergrade
   Black Rat Snake x Yellow
   Rat Snake
   Elaphe o. obsoleta x Elaphe
   obsoleta quadrivittata
   Photo by H. B. Bechtel
B. Interspecific
   Eastern Diamondback x Timber
   Rattlesnake
   Crotalus adamanteus x
   Crotalus horridus
   Photo by Bill Love/Glades Herp Inc.

A.

A. Corn Snake x California
Kingsnake
*Elaphe g. guttata x
Lampropeltis getula
californiae*
Photo by Kevin Enge

B. Corn Snake x Sonora
Gopher Snake
*Elaphe g. guttata x Pituophis
melanoleucus affinis*
Photo by H. B. Bechtel

B.

Index to Illustrations by Scientific Name

Index to Illustrations by Common Name

Index